Traffic Signs Manual

Chapter 5

Road Markings

Department for Transport

Department for Regional Development (Northern Ireland)

Scottish Executive

Welsh Assembly Government

London: TSO

Traffic Signs Manual 2003

Contents of Chapters 1-8

* To be published

Published for the Department for Transport under licence from the
Controller of Her Majesty's Stationery Office

ISBN - 0 11 552479 7

Printed in Great Britain using material containing 55% post-consumer waste, 20% post-industrial waste and 25% ECF pulp.

Chapter 5

CONTENTS

1 INTRODUCTION

GENERAL

1.1 The Traffic Signs Manual is intended to give advice to traffic authorities and their agents on the correct use of signs and road markings. Mandatory requirements are set out in the current version of the Traffic Signs Regulations and General Directions; nothing in the manual can override these. The advice is given to assist authorities in the discharge of their duties under section 122 of the Road Traffic Regulation Act 1984, but it is for traffic authorities to determine what signing they consider necessary to meet those duties.

1.2 The Traffic Signs Manual is applicable in England, Northern Ireland, Scotland and Wales. References to "the Secretary of State" should therefore be interpreted as referring to the Secretary of State for Transport, the Department for Regional Development (Northern Ireland), the Scottish Executive or the Welsh Assembly Government as appropriate.

1.3 This chapter of the manual describes the design and use of road markings (including road studs), i.e. markings on the surface of the road for the control, warning, guidance or information of road users. Some markings may be used to supplement upright signs; others are intended to be used alone.

1.4 Any reference to a "Chapter" is a reference to a Chapter of the Traffic Signs Manual, e.g. Chapter 3 for regulatory signs or Chapter 4 for warning signs and any reference to a "section", unless otherwise stated, is a reference to a section in this chapter of the manual. Where more detailed background information might be helpful, reference is made to Departmental Standards and Advice Notes. These can be found in the Design Manual for Roads and Bridges, published by the Stationery Office.

1.5 Any reference to "the Regulations" or "the Directions" is a reference to the Traffic Signs Regulations and General Directions 2002 and applicable to England, Scotland and Wales. Reference to a "diagram number" is a reference to a diagram in those Regulations. In Northern Ireland the relevant legislation is the Traffic Signs Regulations (Northern Ireland) 1997. Diagram and regulation numbering occasionally differs in the Northern Ireland Regulations (see Appendix A). References to Directions are not applicable in Northern Ireland; where these are referred to, advice should be sought from the Department for Regional Development's Roads Service Headquarters.

USE OF ROAD MARKINGS

1.6 Road markings serve a very important function in conveying to road users information and requirements which might not be possible using upright signs. They have the advantage that they can often be seen when a verge-mounted sign is obscured, and, unlike such signs, they can provide a continuing message.

1.7 Road markings have their limitations. They may be completely obliterated by snow. Their conspicuity is impaired when wet or dirty, and their effective life is reduced if they are subjected to heavy trafficking.

1.8 Nevertheless, road markings make a vital contribution to safety, e.g. by clearly defining the path to be followed through hazards, by separating conflicting movements and by delineating the road edge on unlit roads at night. They can also help to improve junction capacity, and make best use of available road space. In particular, widespread use of lane markings is desirable; by encouraging lane discipline they improve the safety and efficiency of traffic flow. Longitudinal lines should be designed to ensure a flowing alignment, avoiding sudden changes of direction or sharp tapers of inadequate length. Road marking layout should always be considered in detail at the design stage of any scheme.

1.9 Because of the oblique angle at which they are viewed, road markings appear heavily foreshortened. This effect is countered in the case of worded markings, e.g. SLOW, by elongating the legend (see paras 22.47 to 22.49). Two sizes are prescribed; the larger marking is legible at a greater distance and is used where traffic speeds are higher. Similarly, longitudinal lines need to be wider and longer where speeds are high, in order to maintain adequate conspicuity.

VISIBILITY

1.10 For road markings to be effective, they must be clearly visible both by day and by night. Markings have two principal functions. The first is symbolic, e.g. hatched markings; the driver needs to have learned that these indicate an area which is not available to traffic. The second is guidance; centre lines, edge lines and lane lines help drivers to maintain their lateral position on the road. Some markings, e.g. hazard lines and double white line systems have both symbolic and guidance functions.

1.11 The guidance function is less critical (although still important) in daylight or on lit roads because there are many visual cues available to enable the driver to judge course and position. On unlit roads at night, conditions are very different; the visual stimuli in the distance and to the sides of the road are largely absent. Road markings then become the most important aid in enabling the driver to follow the road.

1.12 Recent collaborative European research has shown that drivers need to be able to detect guidance markings at a distance equivalent to a minimum of two seconds of travel time. If the visibility is less than this, drivers tend to adjust too late when the road changes direction. They run too close to the centre line on left hand bends, or too close to the road edge on right hand bends. The higher the prevailing traffic speed, the greater the visibility distance required to maintain this two-second "preview time". If it is not provided, drivers tend to miss the curve, or proceed in a series of staggers.

1.13 A variety of factors influence the visibility distance of a road marking. It is increased when a line is wider, has a higher mark-to-gap ratio or has a higher coefficient of retroreflected luminance (in the day time, higher contrast with the road surface). Visibility distance is adversely affected by glare from oncoming vehicles, dirty headlamps or windscreen and especially by rain; the glass beads which produce the night time luminance are drowned by excess water, greatly reducing the brightness of the line. Older drivers also see a marking less well than the young; someone seventy years old may suffer a reduction in visibility distance of more than 20% compared with drivers still in their twenties.

1.14 The marking regime prescribed in the UK generally gives adequate levels of guidance in good conditions, i.e. where the road is dry, the driver is young, the vehicle has clean, powerful headlamps and there is no glare from oncoming vehicles. On roads with high traffic speeds, wider lines should normally be adopted where alternatives are prescribed. However, it is important that guidance markings are well maintained. Severe wear reduces both effective width and retroreflective performance, and hence the visibility distance. Further guidance on the maintenance of road markings can be found in paras 23.21 to 23.26.

REFLECTORISATION

1.15 Tiny glass beads are incorporated in road markings so that they reflect the light from vehicle headlamps back towards the driver. This makes the marking much brighter at night than non-reflectorised materials. The new European Standard for road markings (BS EN 1436) specifies several different classes for night-time brightness. Brighter markings are visible at greater distances, and may provide an acceptable level of performance for a longer time before renewal becomes necessary (see paras 23.9, 23.10 and 23.16 for further details).

1.16 Markings which maintain night-time performance even when wet may also be specified. This is usually achieved by the use of larger glass beads, but the wet performance of certain road markings may also be enhanced by the use of raised profiles (see paras 4.39 to 4.48, and 23.16).

DIMENSIONS

1.17 Dimensions on the figures are in millimetres unless stated otherwise. Many markings are fully dimensioned in the Regulations. Detailed drawings of the more complex ones are published by the Stationery Office in the series "Working Drawings for Traffic Sign Design and Manufacture" and also on the Department's website.

2 LEGAL

PRESCRIBED MARKINGS AND ROAD STUDS

2.1 All road markings placed on a highway or road to which the public have access must be either prescribed by Regulations or authorised by the Secretary of State for Transport (for installations in England) or the Department for Regional Development (Northern Ireland), the Scottish Executive or the Welsh Assembly Government as appropriate.

2.2 All road studs used on the public highway must satisfy the minimum performance classes specified in direction 57 or, if of a type not covered by the European Standard BS EN 1463 (see para 6.6), e.g. light-emitting studs, be approved in writing by the Secretary of State or by the equivalent national authority (see para 1.2).

PLACING OF ROAD MARKINGS AND STUDS

2.3 Road markings and road studs may be placed on a highway only by or with the consent of the highway authority (section 132 of the Highways Act 1980). In Scotland, this will be the appropriate roads authority.

2.4 Certain road markings may be used only if supported by a traffic regulation order or other statutory provision (direction 7), whilst others, e.g. Give Way markings (diagram 1003), have legal implications in that not complying with them could constitute a traffic offence under Section 36 of the Road Traffic Act 1988 (regulation 10). Some road markings may be placed only in conjunction with certain other markings or with specified signs (direction 18).

2.5 Care should be taken to ensure that markings are used only in the manner prescribed in the Regulations, and that no non-prescribed marking is used unless it has been authorised in writing. Failure to do so may leave an authority open to litigation, or make a traffic regulation order unenforceable.

2.6 Regulation 31(3) requires the use of white road studs in conjunction with double white lines (diagrams 1013.1, 1013.3 and 1013.4). Guidance on the more general use of road studs is given in section 6.

2.7 Clarification of current policy on the use of edge of carriageway markings and associated road studs in Northern Ireland should be sought from the Department for Regional Development's Roads Service Headquarters.

ILLUMINATION, COLOURS AND DIMENSIONS

2.8 Most road markings that have a guidance function are required to be illuminated by retroreflecting material (regulation 31(1)). A full list appears in table 23-1.

2.9 Road markings are prescribed in the colours white and yellow. Further details can be found in paras 23.17 and 23.18.

2.10 The colours and location of stud reflectors with respect to the running lanes are prescribed in regulation 31(7) and detailed in paras 6.9 and 6.10.

2.11 In addition to indicating overall dimensions, the Regulations prescribe maximum heights for road markings and road studs (regulation 32).

3 STOP AND GIVE WAY MARKINGS

GENERAL

3.1 The legal requirements imposed on drivers by the STOP sign and its associated marking are defined in regulation 16. The requirements imposed by the Give Way marking are defined in regulation 25.

3.2 The Stop line shown in figure 3-1 and the Give Way line shown in figure 3-2 are normally positioned so that the edge of the marking nearest to the major road continues the line of the edge of that road, even when the minor road enters at an angle other than 90°. See para 3.21 for guidance on positioning the Give Way line where a 1 m hard strip is provided.

3.3 On two-way minor roads, the Stop or Give Way line normally extends to the centre of the carriageway, the remaining width being marked with diagram 1009 indicating the edge of the major road. Where this would result in Stop or Give Way lines less than 2.75 m long, these should be extended across the full width of the minor road carriageway, and the centre line omitted. The diagram 1009 edge marking is not used at traffic signals.

3.4 Where a one-way street enters a major road, the Give Way or Stop marking is always carried across the whole width of the minor road.

3.5 The transverse markings should be accompanied by longitudinal warning lines, indicating the centre line or lane division, extending from the junction in accordance with the standards set out in para 4.16 for approach warning lines.

3.6 The Directions prohibit the use of STOP signs and markings or Give Way lines on all legs of a junction, as this would cause uncertainty as to which vehicles had priority (directions 30 and 34(1)(a)).

TRAFFIC SIGNAL STOP LINE

3.7 The marking (diagram 1001) consists of a single continuous line 200 mm or 300 mm in width and indicates the position beyond which a driver must not proceed when required to stop by light signals. The 200 mm width is generally for use in urban areas. The 300 mm width should be used in rural areas, or where the 85th percentile speed exceeds 35 mph. The greater width may also be used in urban areas at difficult locations, or where heavy traffic results in rapid erosion of the marking.

3.8 The Stop line will normally be at right angles to the centre line of the road to which it applies. It should be at least 1.5 m in advance of the near side primary signal, although 2.5 m is preferable (see para 9.4). Site conditions may necessitate a greater distance (see below). Recommended layouts are shown in figures 9-1 and 9-2.

3.9 It may be necessary to set back the Stop line to allow for positioning of the primary traffic signal and any pedestrian crossing facility. At some junctions it is necessary to set it back a further distance to permit turning movements into that road (see para 9.5). This is likely to reduce the capacity of the junction; an alternative might be to prohibit a turning movement.

3.10 For details of the stop line used at level crossings and at tramways at traffic signal junctions respectively, see paras 19.3 and 18.12. The advanced stop line for cycles (diagram 1001.2) is dealt with in paras 16.20 to 16.22.

JUNCTION STOP LINE

3.11 The marking (diagram 1002.1) consists of a single continuous line 400 mm wide. It is used only at junctions controlled by STOP signs (diagram 601.1) and must not be used with a GIVE WAY sign (see also paras 3.2 to 3.6). The STOP sign, Stop line and the worded STOP marking (diagram 1022) must always be used in conjunction with each other (see figure 3-1). Two sizes for the word STOP are prescribed, as shown in table 3-1.

3.12 The word STOP is normally located so that the top edge of the legend is not more than 2.75 m nor less than 2.1 m from the nearest part of the Stop line. Exceptionally this may be increased to a maximum of 15 m, e.g. where the vertical curvature or a sharp bend prevents it being seen from a distance.

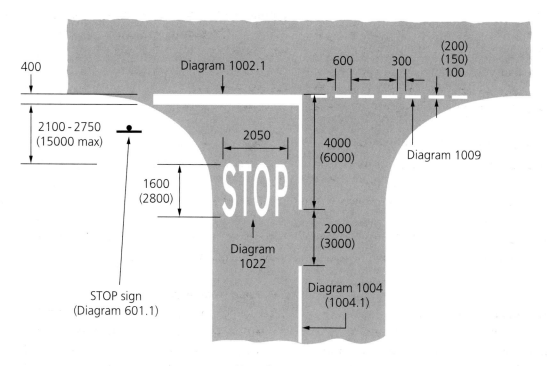

Markings for use with STOP sign

Figure 3-1

3.13 Where advance warning of the STOP sign is required, this is provided by the sign to diagram 501 and its associated distance plate (diagram 502) which may be accompanied by the worded marking SLOW (diagram 1024) on the carriageway. Table 2-1 in Chapter 4 indicates where advance signing is appropriate.

Table 3-1

85 percentile speed (mph)	Size of STOP sign (mm)	Size of STOP road marking (mm)
Up to 30	750	1600
31 to 40	750 (900)	1600 (2800)
41 to 50	900 (1200)	2800
Over 50	1200	2800

NOTE: Alternative sizes are shown in brackets. The alternatives should be used where they are required by site conditions or where the accident record calls for greater emphasis.

GIVE WAY MARKINGS

3.14 The Give Way marking to diagram 1003 is used at major/minor road junctions. It may be accompanied by the approach triangle (diagram 1023) and the upright sign to diagram 602, but in the following combinations only:

(i)   Give Way marking alone

(ii) Give Way marking with approach triangle

(iii) Give Way marking with approach triangle and GIVE WAY sign.

Advance warning of the GIVE WAY using diagrams 501 and 503 (in accordance with the guidance in table 2-1 in Chapter 4) may be provided with (iii), i.e. only when the upright GIVE WAY sign is installed at the junction. In all cases, the worded SLOW road marking may be used in advance of the junction.

3.15 With the exceptions mentioned in para 3.22, the Give Way marking is intended for use at all junctions other than those which are controlled by

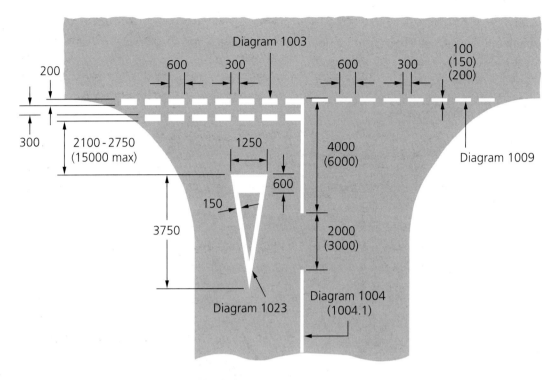

Markings for use with GIVE WAY sign

Figure 3-2

STOP signs or by traffic signals (except for movements not controlled by those signals). It is not generally used at private accesses, or on minor estate roads where traffic speeds and flows are low and visibility is good.

3.16 The prescribed marking (diagram 1003) for major/minor junctions consists of two broken lines laid side by side, each comprising 600 mm marks and 300 mm gaps. The lines are 200 mm wide and are spaced 300 mm apart (see figure 3-2). Subject to the following, the marking is laid at the mouth of the minor road at a junction (see also paras 3.2 to 3.6).

3.17 The triangular marking (diagram 1023) may be used only when a transverse Give Way line to diagram 1003 is provided (see para 3.14). When the junction is with a heavily trafficked route, or the presence of the major road is not obvious, e.g. at a crossroads, the marking should be accompanied by the upright GIVE WAY sign to diagram 602. The upright sign should also be used in rural areas at all junctions of public roads with primary routes, and in urban areas at junctions with primary routes unless the minor road is a residential or local street.

3.18 Diagram 1023 is normally located with its leading edge between 2100 mm and 2750 mm from the transverse marking (see figure 3-2). This distance may be increased to a maximum of 15 m if the vertical sign has to be sited further from the junction in order to ensure adequate visibility (see Chapter 3). The triangle should be positioned approximately in the centre of the traffic lane. Where the approach to the junction comprises more than one lane, the marking should be provided in each lane.

3.19 Alternative dimensions for diagrams 1003 and 1023 are prescribed for use with cycle tracks (see para 16.3).

3.20 The route carrying the highest traffic flow should normally be given priority. Exceptionally, conditions at certain junctions might be such that it would be preferable to treat a road of greater traffic importance as the minor road when allocating priority. For example, at a square crossroads junction, stopping vehicles on a steep downhill grade might result in overrun type accidents. It might also be beneficial to give a less heavily trafficked road priority as a way of overcoming poor visibility to the right.

3.21 On roads where a 1 m hard strip is provided, demarcated with the edge of carriageway marking to diagram 1012.1 or 1012.3, the Give Way marking should be aligned with the back of the hard strip and not with the edge line (see figure 3-3).

3.22 Diagram 1003 should not be used on high speed dual carriageway roads where traffic either joins from a slip road (at a grade separated junction) or there is a merging taper. At such sites the marking to diagram 1010 should be used (see figure 3-4).

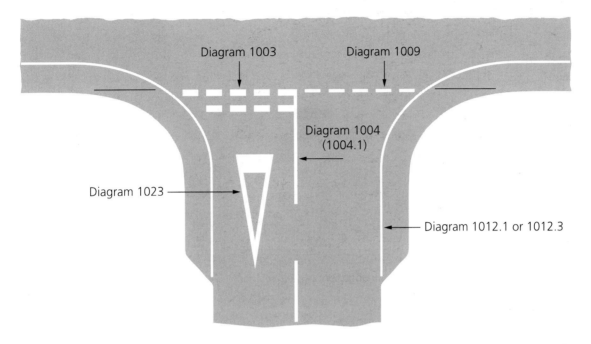

Layout used where a 1 metre hard strip
is provided on the main carriageway

Figure 3-3

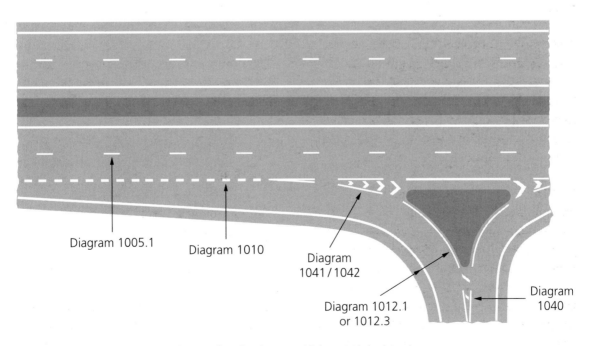

Markings for acceleration lane on high speed dual carriageway

Figure 3-4

3.23 Where a side road joins either a high speed single carriageway road or a dual carriageway road with a gap in the central reservation, the marking to diagram 1003 should be used.

PRIORITY TRAFFIC SITES

3.24 Where the width of the road is such that traffic from one direction is given priority over that from the other using diagrams 615 and 811, the Give Way marking to diagram 1003 may be used with diagram 615 to indicate the place at which vehicles should wait. The marking to diagram 1023 may also be provided, but not the vertical sign to diagram 602, which is prescribed for use only at junctions or level crossings (regulation 16). A longitudinal warning line to diagram 1004 or 1004.1 should be used on the approach to this narrow section as far as the Give Way line, discontinued through the hazard and recommenced where an adequate two-way width is regained. Diagram 615 must be accompanied by the plate to diagram 615.1 "Give way to oncoming vehicles", and diagram 811 must be accompanied by the plate to diagram 811.1 "Priority over oncoming vehicles". Under no circumstances should traffic from both directions be required by the signs or markings to give way.

CYCLE PRIORITY

3.25 Regulation 25(6) enables the marking to diagram 1003 to be used to give priority to a cycle track crossing a road. The length of road crossed by the cycle track must consist of a road hump, which should be of the flat-topped type. The hump must extend across the full width of the carriageway, in accordance with direction 34(2). The marking to diagram 1023 should also be provided, together with a longitudinal warning line to diagram 1004 on each approach. The hump must be marked with diagram 1062 (see para 21.9). The Give Way marking should be placed on the carriageway of the road, not on any part of the hump.

4 LONGITUDINAL LINES

CENTRE LINES

4.1 The 1994 Regulations introduced new markings intended for use as centre lines separating opposing flows of traffic on single carriageway roads. These are illustrated in figure 4-1 and the dimensions and recommended applications are shown in table 4-1. Diagram 1008 is used where the speed limit is 40 mph or less, and 1008.1 where the speed limit is more than 40 mph.

4.2 All new installations and reinstatements must use diagrams 1008 and 1008.1 for centre line markings (where warning lines and double line systems are not appropriate) in place of old markings to diagram 1005.

4.3 The marking should be used only on single carriageway roads. Where the road comprises one lane in each direction, the 100 mm wide marking will normally be sufficient. On four-lane roads, three-lane marked as two in one direction and one in the other, or two-lane 10 m wide, the 150 mm marking should be used. Any lane lines should be 100 mm wide (see paras 4.7 to 4.11). The centre line should never be narrower than the lane line (see para 4.10). It may be

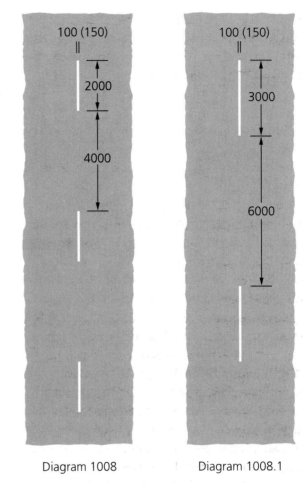

Diagram 1008   Diagram 1008.1

Figure 4-1

Table 4-1 Centre line on single carriageway roads

Diag No.	Speed limit (mph)	Mark (m)	Gap (m)	Width (mm)	Spacing of studs (if used) (m)	Description
1008	40 or less	2	4	100	12	Two-lane roads, not less than 5.5 m in width
1008	40 or less	2	4	150	6	Two-lane roads 10 m or more in width (or three lanes marked as two in one direction and one in the other) Four lanes or more (see para 4.3)
1008.1	Over 40	3	6	100	18	Two-lane roads, not less than 5.5 m in width
1008.1	Over 40	3	6	150	9	Two-lane roads 10 m or more in width (or three lanes marked as two in one direction and one in the other) Four lanes or more (see para 4.3)

replaced by the warning line (see paras 4.12 to 4.26) where appropriate. When there are two or more lanes in each direction, consideration might be given to double white lines (see section 5).

4.4 Where forward visibility is restricted (see para 4.16) or on the approach to some other hazard (e.g. a roundabout or other junction), the centre line marking should be replaced with warning lines to diagrams 1004 or 1004.1 (see figure 4-3). These are the inverse of the mark/gap dimensions for the centre line and therefore maintain the same module (see table 4-3 for the minimum number of marks).

4.5 On two or four lane roads the marking should normally be laid in the geometric centre. It can however be laid off-centre to allow parking along one side. Where it is necessary to change the position of lines in relation to the centre of the road, the deflection should be smooth and made at the inclinations specified in table 14-1.

4.6 On rural roads below 5.5 m in width, over-running of the carriageway edge can occur if centre line markings are provided, causing maintenance problems. Drivers might also expect a road marked with a centre line to be wide enough for opposing lanes of traffic to pass. In these circumstances the centre line should be omitted, but it would be helpful if edge of carriageway markings are then used.

LANE LINES

4.7 Lane lines (see figure 4-2) ensure that available carriageway space is used to its maximum capacity. In helping vehicles to maintain a consistent lateral position, they also offer safety benefits and should be used wherever practicable.

4.8 The marking is intended for dividing the carriageway into lanes where traffic on either side of the line travels in the same direction, and not for separating opposing flows of traffic. Details are set out in table 4-2.

4.9 Lane lines on the approach to Give Way and Stop markings, including roundabouts and traffic signals, should change to warning lines in accordance with table 4-3 and para 4.24.

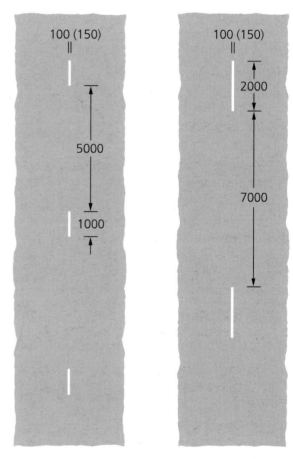

Diagram 1005   Diagram 1005.1

Figure 4-2

Table 4-2 Lane lines

Diagram No.	Speed limit (mph)	Mark (m)	Gap (m)	Width (mm)	Spacing of studs (if used) (m)
1005	40 or less	1	5	100 (150)	12
1005.1	Over 40	2	7	100 (150)	18

4.10 On single carriageway roads with more than two lanes, the centre line should normally be of a greater width than the lane lines. This is particularly important when the warning module is used for both, making it more difficult to determine which line divides the opposing traffic streams.

4.11 On 70 mph dual carriageway all-purpose roads and on motorways, the wider (150 mm) marking should be used as this increases its visibility distance. It is also likely to be of benefit on concrete roads, even with a lower speed limit, helping to compensate for the reduced contrast.

WARNING LINES

4.12 Warning lines are detailed in figure 4-3 and table 4-3. They are used:

(i) as centre lines at bends and crests, and on multi-lane roads (see paras 4.16 to 4.18),

(ii) as centre lines where it is necessary to highlight the presence of a road junction, central refuge or other hazard (see paras 4.19 to 4.23),

(iii) approaching or through junctions (see para 4.24 and sections 7, 8, 9 and 10),

(iv) to mark the boundary of advisory cycle lanes (see paras 16.9 and 16.10), and

(v) over road humps (see para 21.10).

4.13 Warning lines are always single; they must never be used as part of a double line installation, and must not be formed of raised rib markings (see paras 4.39 to 4.48).

4.14 Two patterns of warning line are prescribed, each having alternative widths of 100 or 150 mm. The wider line is visible at a greater distance, and should be used where this might be beneficial, e.g. at particularly hazardous sites (see also para 4.10). The two standard modules are 6 metres and 9 metres in length (the combination of one mark and one gap)

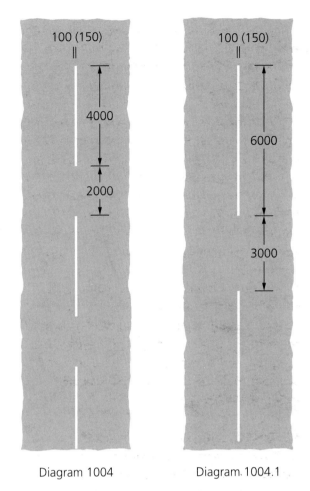

Diagram 1004   Diagram 1004.1

Figure 4-3

depending on the speed limit. Table 4-3 sets out appropriate arrangements for various road layouts and speed limits.

4.15 Overuse of the marking should be avoided. Its use where it is not justified will devalue its effect. Particular care should be taken in urban areas where there might be a temptation to use it extensively.

4.16 Warning lines are used in place of centre lines where forward visibility is less than the warning line visibility distance W indicated in table 4-4. This is based on the visibility necessary for safe overtaking on a two-way carriageway (see para 5.22 for the definition of visibility distance). For intermediate speeds, the appropriate visibility distance should be taken as the higher figure between the steps shown, e.g. for an 85th percentile speed of 45 mph, warning lines are justified when visibility is between 120 and 195 m. Where the visibility distance is less than the desirable minimum V, a double white line system should be considered (see section 5).

4.17 Where warning lines are used to separate opposing flows of traffic on single carriageway roads, they should normally be laid in the geometric centre of the carriageway (see also para 4.5).

4.18 On four-lane roads the 150 mm wide warning line may be used to separate opposing traffic, although consideration might be given to the use of double white lines (see section 5). On three-lane roads marked with two lanes in one direction and one in the other, the 150 mm wide line should be used, together with 100 mm wide lane lines. The lane line should never be wider than the warning line.

4.19 Warning lines may be used to highlight the presence of a road junction (see section 7 for further guidance) and to mark the approach to central refuges or other hazards, (see para 4.23), except where these are within a double line section.

4.20 On straight sections of road, warning lines on the priority route would normally be appropriate when the average traffic volume from the side road exceeds about 100 vehicles per hour. However, warning lines will be justified at lower traffic volumes where visibility of the junction is impaired.

Table 4-3 Warning lines

Diag No.	Speed limit (mph)	Mark (m)	Gap (m)	Width (mm)	Spacing of studs (if used) (m)	Minimum number of marks on each approach Speed limit (mph)			Purpose
						30	40	Over 40	
1004	40 or less	4	2	100	6	5	7	-	Central warning line on two-lane roads less than 10 m wide
1004.1	Over 40	6	3	100	9	-	-	7	
1004	40 or less	4	2	150	6	5	7	-	Central warning line on two-lane roads 10 m or more wide
1004.1	Over 40	6	3	150	9	-	-	7	
1004	40 or less	4	2	150	6	7	10	-	Central warning line on four or six-lane single carriageway roads
1004.1	Over 40	6	3	150	9	-	-	10	
1004	40 or less	4	2	100	6	5	7	-	Lane line on all roads on approach to roundabouts or signal controlled junctions, and the minor road approaching a priority junction
	50	6	3	100	9	-	-	7	
1004.1	60	6	3	100	9	-	-	7	
	70	6	3	150	9	-	-	7	

NOTE: These markings may also be used to delineate an advisory cycle lane (see para 16.9).

Table 4-4 Visibility distances

85 percentile speed (mph)	Desirable minimum visibility distance V (m)	Warning line visibility distance W (m)
Up to 30	75	115
31 to 40	95	160
41 to 50	120	195
51 to 60	150	240
Over 60	175	275

4.21 The minor road should be marked with at least the minimum number of marks shown in table 4-3. On narrow two-way minor roads where the Give Way or Stop marking is extended over the whole width (see para 3.3), a warning line is not provided.

4.22 If the minor road is a one-way street, a warning line on the major road will normally be needed only if the direction of flow is towards the major road. The principal purpose of the marking is to warn drivers of the risk of unseen vehicles emerging.

4.23 A warning line approaching a refuge, central reservation etc. should be inclined for its full length (see table 4-3 for the minimum number of marks), terminating in a position offset 300 mm from the edge of the refuge (see figure 4-4). This may be reduced when the speed limit is 40 mph or less and there is limited width between the island and the near side kerb, but should preferably not be less

than 150 mm. Kerb faces will not normally exceed 75 mm, because of the risk of loss of control if struck by a vehicle. Where unusually high kerbs are used, the 300 mm clearance should always be provided. When the length of taper required to comply with table 14-1 needs more marks than the minimum specified in table 4-3, the number of marks should be increased sufficiently to ensure that the entire taper length uses the warning module. Guidance on the use of hatched markings for additional emphasis is given in paras 4.49 to 4.51 and further advice on the treatment of refuges in section 14.

4.24 On dual carriageway roads, or single carriageway roads with two or more lanes in one direction, warning lines should be used in place of lane lines on the immediate approach to signal controlled junctions or roundabouts. Where additional lanes are introduced on the immediate approach to a roundabout it might not be possible to provide the minimum number of marks. In such cases as many marks as possible should be used without reducing any lane width below 2 m at the start of the taper (see para 8.3). The detailed arrangements for marking roundabouts and signal controlled junctions are described in sections 8 and 9 respectively.

4.25 The number of marks recommended in table 4-3 is the minimum on each approach, although this is not always possible on minor roads. The number of marks should be extended wherever justified by road or traffic conditions; the marking can with benefit be extended to start at the location of the accompanying warning sign. Figure 4-5 indicates

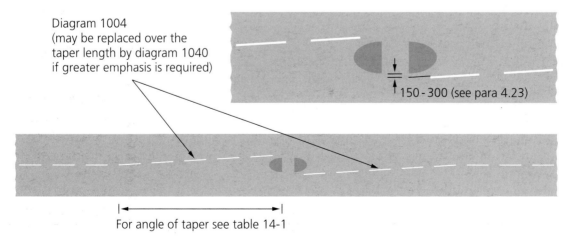

Diagram 1004
(may be replaced over the
taper length by diagram 1040
if greater emphasis is required)

150 - 300 (see para 4.23)

For angle of taper see table 14-1

Figure 4-4

a possible combination of signs and markings at a road junction. This arrangement is not intended to be used at all junctions, but may be appropriate at difficult sites where, for example, overtaking may cause a problem on the approach to a junction.

4.26 Where there are two features that would justify warning lines (e.g. two junctions, or a junction followed by a bend), then a short length of standard centre line between two warning lines can help to highlight the separate hazards, even if this results in fewer than the minimum number of marks being provided for the second hazard.

EDGE OF CARRIAGEWAY LINES

4.27 The following types are prescribed:

   (i)   diagram 1009 (see figure 4-6, para 4.28 and table 4-5),

   (ii) diagram 1010 (see figure 4-7, paras 4.29 and 4.30 and table 4-5),

   (iii) diagram 1012.1 (see figure 4-8, paras 4.31 to 4.38 and table 4-5 and, when used at level crossings, para 19.9), and

   (iv) diagrams 1012.2 and 1012.3 (see paras 4.39 to 4.48, table 4-5 and figure 4-9).

4.28 Diagram 1009 should be used to extend the transverse Give Way and Stop line markings across the entry half width of the minor road as illustrated in figures 3-1 and 3-2. It is used across the full width if the minor road is one-way away from the junction. The normal width of the line is 100 mm but when it is used in conjunction with a continuous edge line, the width should be varied to match. The marking may be used as an alternative to diagram 1010 across private driveways where the larger marking would be impracticable, e.g. because of the narrowness of the entrance. Where the width of the minor road is such that Give Way or Stop lines would be less than 2.75 m long, these should be extended across the whole width of the road (see para 3.3). The use of diagram 1009 at the start of cycle lanes is dealt with in paras 16.6, 16.8 and 16.10.

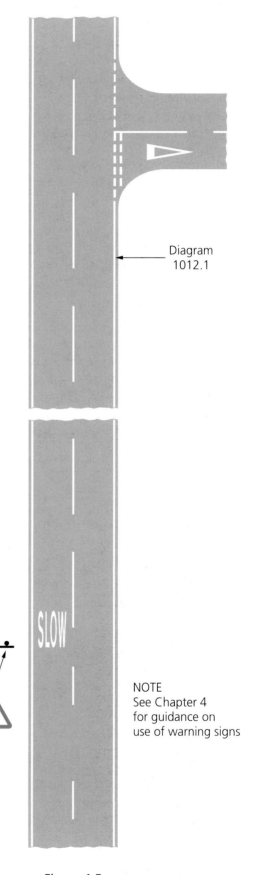

Diagram 1012.1

NOTE
See Chapter 4 for guidance on use of warning signs

Figure 4-5

4.29 Diagram 1010 is used instead of diagram 1009 at lay-bys and at acceleration and deceleration splays, and also for emphasising lane drops. Details of the various prescribed uses are set out in table 4-5. The marking may be supplemented with uni-directional reflecting road studs, at the spacing shown in table 4-5. Green reflectors should be used at lane drops, along acceleration and deceleration lanes and at lay-bys.

4.30 Further guidance on the use of diagram 1010 can be found in:

section 7 for major/minor junctions,
section 10 for grade separated junctions,
section 17 for bus lanes,
section 18 for tram markings, and
section 22 for low bridges.

4.31 Diagram 1012.1 is intended for general use to delineate the edge of carriageway, particularly on unlit classified roads and those not having clearly defined raised kerbs. It should also normally be used on all-purpose roads with hard shoulders or hard strips, on motorways, unless profiled edge lines are used (see paras 4.39 to 4.48) and to delineate footways at level crossings (see para 19.9).

4.32 Trials have shown that edge markings have merit as a safety measure despite their efficiency sometimes being impaired by dirt because of their location near the edge of the carriageway. They can also help to protect verges on narrow rural roads.

4.33 The marking should be laid with a gap of approximately 225 mm to the near side edge of the carriageway. The continuous line should not be carried across the mouths of side roads, acceleration or deceleration splays, gaps in the central reservation or lay-bys, where lines to diagrams 1009 or 1010 should be used.

4.34 Where the carriageway is less than 5.5 m in width, the centre line should be omitted (see para 4.6) but edge lines, where used, continued. Where edge lines are not already in use, their introduction over the length where the centre line is interrupted will help draw attention to the hazard.

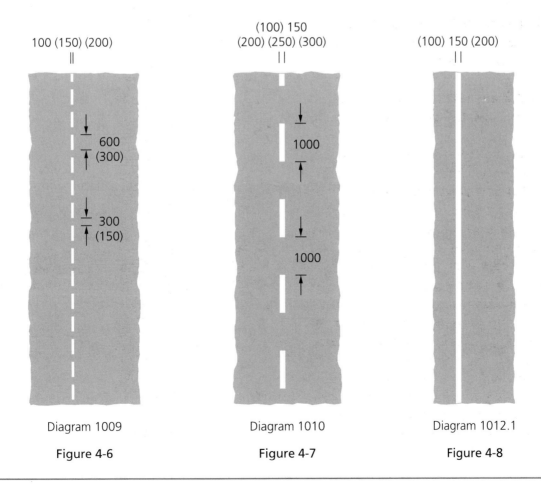

Diagram 1009	Diagram 1010	Diagram 1012.1
Figure 4-6	Figure 4-7	Figure 4-8

Table 4-5 Edge of carriageway markings

Diag No.	Mark (m)	Gap (m)	Width (mm) Speed limit (mph)			Spacing of studs (if used) (m)	Description
			40 or less	50 or 60	70		
1009	600	300	See para 4.28			Not used	Edge of carriageway at a road junction when a Give Way or Stop marking is used, or field entrance or exit from a private drive onto a public road
	300	150	100	100	100	Not used	Edge of carriageway at a junction of a cycle track and another road
	600	300	150	200	200	Not used	Diagonal marking at the start of a cycle lane (see also section 16)
1010	1000	1000	100	150	200	8	Edge of carriageway at a road junction when a Give Way or Stop marking is not used, or exit from a private drive onto a public road, or at a lay-by
	1000	1000	250 or 300	250 or 300	250 or 300	Not used	Start of a bus lane or interruption of a with-flow lane at a left turn (see figure 17-1). The line width will match the associated marking to diagram 1049
	1000	1000	100	150	200	Not used	To show the most suitable path for vehicles through an arch bridge
	1000	1000	100	150	200	Not used	Edge of part of a carriageway used by tramcars
	1000	1000	100	150	200	See para 10.11	Division between the main carriageway and a traffic lane which leaves at a junction ahead (lane drop)
1012.1	Continuous		100	100	150	Not normally used	All-purpose roads with no hard shoulder or hard strip
			150	150	200	18	All-purpose roads with hard shoulder or hard strip
			200	200	200	18	Motorways
1012.2	Continuous		200	200	200	18	Motorways
1012.3	Continuous		150 or 200	150 or 200	150 or 200	18	All-purpose roads with hard strip or hard shoulder. The 200 mm wide line must be used when there is a hard shoulder

NOTE: The prescribed colours for road studs and further guidance on spacing are detailed in paras 6.9 to 6.14.

4.35 The following are examples of situations where the edge of carriageway marking might be particularly appropriate:

    (i)   where the demarcation between the carriageway and the verge is poor,

    (ii)   along lengths prone to fog and mist,

    (iii)   on heavily-trafficked single carriageway roads where headlamp dazzle is severe,

    (iv)   at sudden changes of carriageway width,

    (v)   on the approaches to narrow bridges,

    (vi)   on the approaches to bends indicated by bend warning signs,

    (vii)   at the back of a hard shoulder for use during contra-flow working. A 100 mm wide marking is prescribed for this purpose, and is generally laid 50 mm from the back of the hard shoulder. It may remain when the contra-flow has been removed, or

    (viii)   at traffic calming measures e.g. chicanes.

4.36 Edge lines are also recommended for use along the off side carriageway edge of unlit dual carriageway roads. The line should be laid with a gap of approximately 225 mm to the central reservation. The marking should not be carried across right turn lanes or breaks in the central reservation, where lines to diagram 1010 should be used. Where there is a hard strip, edge lines should be laid as indicated in figure 4-19. They should be used on all motorways in the positions shown in figure 4-20.

4.37 Where, because of the traffic importance or nature of the road, clearer delineation is required, red, uni-directional reflecting road studs may be used on the near side edge (see table 4-5) and, on dual carriageway roads, amber adjacent to the central reservation (see also para 6.10).

4.38 When depressible studs are used, they should always be placed on the carriageway side of the edge line to facilitate the cleaning action of the lenses. Non-depressible studs also benefit from trafficking to keep them free from road dirt and maintain their performance. Except at locations where experience has shown that placing the studs on the carriageway side of the edge line reduces their operational life to unacceptable levels, this may be better than placing them behind the line. Further guidance on the use of road studs is given in section 6.

RAISED PROFILE EDGE LINES

4.39 Raised profile lines are prescribed for use as an alternative to the edge of carriageway marking to diagram 1012.1. They consist of a continuous line marking with ribs across the line at regular intervals (see figure 4-9). The vertical edges of the raised ribs stand clear of the water film in wet conditions, improving retroreflective performance under headlight illumination. The ribs also provide an audible vibratory warning to drivers should they stray from the carriageway and run onto the marking.

4.40 Two types are specified, diagram 1012.2 for use on motorways and diagram 1012.3 for use on all-purpose roads with a hard strip or hard shoulder. The base marking must be no more than 6 mm high. The upstand of the ribs above the base marking must not exceed 11 mm for diagram 1012.2 and 8 mm for diagram 1012.3. The 500 mm spacing is suitable for most edge lines laid on the main carriageway. On motorways, the 250 mm spacing is recommended for use on slip roads. The closer spacing helps to maintain the rumble effect, offsetting the likely lower speed. Closer spacing is not used on all-purpose roads as it could present a hazard to cyclists. Diagram 1012.2 is always 200 mm wide. Diagram 1012.3 is usually 150 mm wide but is increased to 200 mm on all-purpose roads with hard shoulders.

4.41 Diagram 1012.3 is used on all-purpose roads, as the more aggressive rib of diagram 1012.2 has an unacceptable effect on cyclists and pedestrians.

4.42 The edge lines of the following diagrams may also make use of raised profile lines:

(i) diagram 1040.3 - reduction of the number of lanes available,

(ii) diagram 1040.5 - approach to a termination of the hard shoulder, and

(iii) diagrams 1042 and 1042.1 - chevron marking, when used between main carriageway and slip road, or between bifurcating or converging carriageways (but not at a roundabout).

4.43 Raised profile markings must not be used as part of any marking or in any circumstances other than as specified above.

4.44 Raised profile markings should be discontinued where pedestrians and cyclists cross the road (e.g. at refuges) or at other places where cyclists are likely to cross them. A plain edge line to diagram 1012.1 should be used instead. This should normally extend a minimum distance of 1 m either side of the crossing point.

4.45 Where gullies or similar features occur in the hard strip, cyclists may need to cross the adjacent edge line marking in order to avoid them. Any raised profile marking adjacent to such features should be replaced with a plain edge line for a distance of 10 m on each side of the gully.

4.46 When raised profile markings are laid on a curve of less than 1000 m radius, motorcyclists may find themselves in difficulty if there is a wide hard strip or hard shoulder and they are tempted to cross onto it. The raised ribs tend to destabilise two-wheeled vehicles on appreciable bends. If there is any concern that motorcycles might frequently cut across the line, the ribs may be omitted, although the improved night-time wet weather visibility will obviously not then be available.

4.47 Drainage gaps of 100 to 150 mm should be provided at intervals of approximately 36 m where the longitudinal fall is flatter than 1 in 150, and there is a crossfall towards the profiled marking.

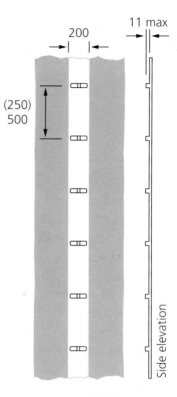

Diagram 1012.2
(for use on motorways)

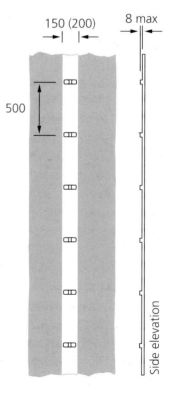

Diagram 1012.3
(for use on all purpose roads with hard strips)

Figure 4-9

4.48 When raised profile markings are renewed, care must be taken to ensure that the rib height is not increased above the maximum height permitted by the Regulations.

HATCHED MARKINGS

4.49 Hatched markings are prescribed as diagrams 1040, 1040.2, 1040.3, 1040.4 and 1040.5. They are also prescribed in diagrams 1013.3 and 1013.4 (see section 5 and paras 7.11 and 7.12). Two sets of dimensions are prescribed where the boundary line is broken, and are as set out in table 4-3 for diagrams 1004 and 1004.1, i.e. a 4 m mark and 2 m gap where the speed limit is 40 mph or less, and 6 m mark and 3 m gap where the speed limit is more than 40 mph. Regulation 12(4) exempts these diagrams from the requirement that alternative dimensions should correspond in order to maintain the shape of the marking. This allows the width of the boundary lines to be matched to those of the centre line or warning line at either end of the hatched marking. The spacing of the diagonal marks is linked to the length of the boundary lines; the closer spacing and the wider diagonal mark is used with the longer lines.

4.50 The tapers should be applied to each side of the centre line, whether it is straight or curved, at the rates specified in table 14-1. Diagrams 1040, 1040.3 and 1040.4 may be preceded by the deflection arrow to diagram 1014 (see figures 4-13 and 13-6, and table 4-6). Arrows used with diagram 1040 should be positioned in the centre line and not in the opposing carriageway as with double white lines, i.e. as shown in figure 5-2 and not as in figure 5-3.

4.51 Diagram 1040 (figure 4-10) is intended to divide opposing flows of traffic on two-way roads. It may be used on the approach to refuges as a more emphatic alternative to the warning line, or to lead into diagram 1040.2. Where road studs are used, they must be white, and should be uni-directional. In diagrams 1040 and 1040.2, one of the boundary lines is omitted when the marking is placed alongside diagram 1049 delineating a bus or cycle lane.

4.52 Diagram 1040.2 (figure 4-11) may be used to separate opposing flows of traffic where the warning

line is considered insufficient at hazards such as a bend or the brow of a hill. Unless this marking starts at a physical obstruction, e.g. a refuge, it should always be preceded by the tapered marking to diagram 1040. See paras 7.2 to 7.12 for guidance on the use of hatched markings at a road junction.

4.53 Diagram 1040.3 (figure 4-12) indicates the approach to a place on a motorway, dual carriageway road or slip road where the number of lanes is reduced, or an area of carriageway not available to traffic. It is bounded by a 200 mm wide continuous edge marking which may be varied to diagram 1012.2 or 1012.3. It may also be varied to 150 mm wide when used on all-purpose roads without hard shoulders. The layout for a main carriageway is shown in figure 4-13 (see figure 10-4 for slip roads).

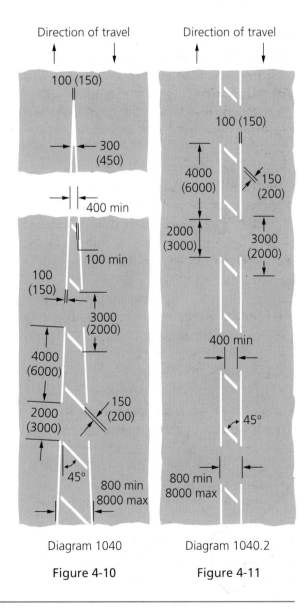

Diagram 1040   Diagram 1040.2

Figure 4-10   **Figure 4-11**

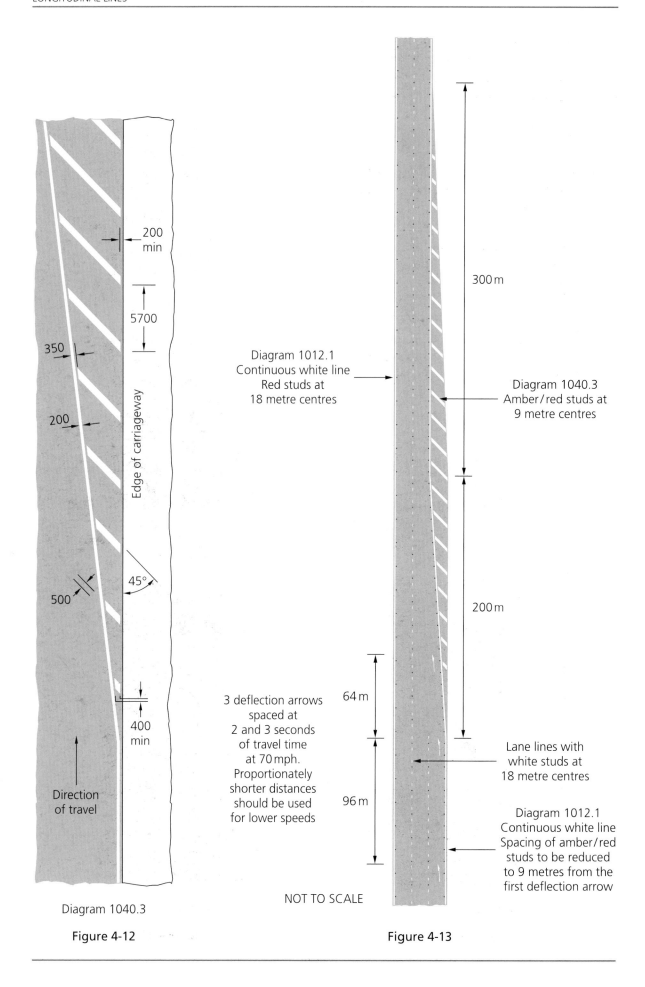

Figure 4-12

Figure 4-13

The studs at the edge line should remain amber and the spacing should be reduced to 9 m along the length of road from the first deflection arrow encountered and along the hatching. Vertical signs to diagrams 872.1/876 should also be used in advance of the taper.

4.54 Diagram 1040.4 (figure 4-14) is used to mark off an area at the edge of the carriageway which drivers should not enter unless it is safe to do so. It will commonly be used to guide traffic past build-outs in traffic calming schemes (see section 21). The tapers are set out in table 4-6; the shape of the marking may be varied to suit the road geometry, provided that the dimensions prescribed in diagram 1040.4 are maintained, and may be reversed. The boundary to the left of the hatched area may be formed by diagram 1049 delineating the off-side edge of a cycle lane.

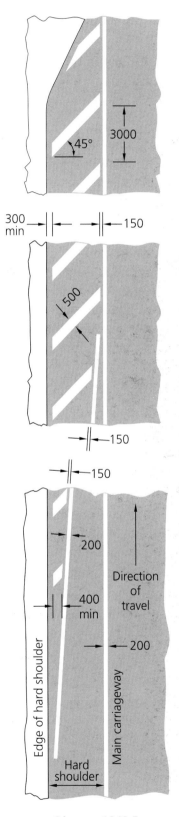

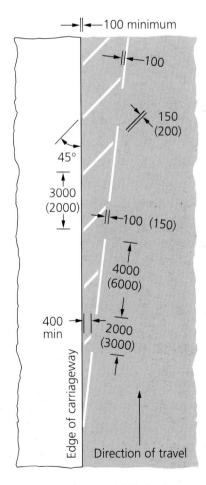

Diagram 1040.4

Figure 4-14

Diagram 1040.5

Figure 4-15

4.55 The marking to diagram 1040.5 (figure 4-15) should be used to indicate the termination of the hard shoulder. The edge marking is always 200 mm wide, whether it is used on motorways or on all-purpose roads with full width hard shoulders. Both longitudinal lines may be formed by the marking to diagram 1012.2 or 1012.3 as appropriate. Where there are two terminations in quick succession, the hard shoulder between them should be hatched off to discourage its use, as rejoining the motorway from the isolated section is likely to be difficult.

END OF DUAL CARRIAGEWAY

4.56 When a dual carriageway road changes to a single carriageway road other than at a junction, traffic should be guided into the slower lane when leaving the dual carriageway section. Details of appropriate vertical signing can be found in figures 5-1 and 5-2 of Chapter 4.

4.57 The reduction in the number of lanes and the taper to a single carriageway should be achieved using hatching to diagrams 1040 and 1040.4. The boundary is derived as follows (see figure 4-16):

(i) the traffic leaving the dual carriageway section should be reduced to a single lane by marking off the outside lane at the inclinations shown in table 4-6. The full reduction should be achieved no later than the end of the central reservation, although it may occur earlier,

(ii) from the point in line with the end of the central reservation, derived in (i), the boundary should continue to the centre line of the single carriageway section at a taper no sharper than that used in (i) above; if the dual carriageway section leads into a right hand bend, it might be better to use a longer taper length in order to merge tangentially with the apex,

(iii) for the carriageway leading to the dual carriageway section, the boundary line should extend from the end of the taper in (ii) to the central reservation.

4.58 The lane line on the leaving carriageway (and the associated white road studs if used) should be omitted over the length of the taper, and two deflection arrows (diagram 1014) should be laid in the centre of the lane to be lost, in advance of the taper at the distances shown in table 4-6. The lane line between the start of the taper and the second arrow upstream of it should be replaced by a warning line to diagram 1004 or 1004.1 as appropriate (see paras 4.12 to 4.26).

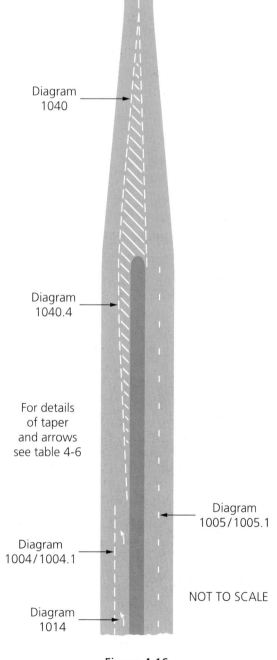

Diagram 1040

Diagram 1040.4

For details of taper and arrows see table 4-6

Diagram 1005/1005.1

Diagram 1004/1004.1

NOT TO SCALE

Diagram 1014

Figure 4-16

Table 4-6 Taper and arrow details

85 percentile speed (mph)	Taper	Length of arrow (m)	Distance from tip of arrow to start of taper (m)		
			First arrow	Second arrow	Third arrow
Up to 30	1 in 40	4.5	13.75	43.75	79.75
31 to 40	1 in 40	4.5	19.75	55.75	109.75
41 to 50	1 in 45	6	21.00	66.00	138.00
51 to 60	1 in 50	6	30.00	84.00	165.00
61 to 70	1 in 55	9	37.50	91.50	190.50

NOTE: Different requirements apply to taper and arrow details for diagram 1040.3; see figure 4-13.

4.59 If road studs are used on the dual carriageway section, near side red studs should be continued through the merge. Amber studs should be used with the boundary line to diagram 1040.4; beyond the end of the central reservation the studs should revert to white, but be uni-directional.

CHEVRON MARKINGS

4.60 Diagram 1041 (figure 4-17) and its parallel-sided version (diagram 1041.1) are intended to separate streams of traffic travelling in the same direction, e.g. on the approach to a junction or to a pedestrian refuge in a one-way street. One of the boundary lines is omitted where the marking is

placed alongside diagram 1049 delineating a bus or cycle lane.

4.61 Diagram 1042 (figure 4-18) is intended for use between a motorway or high standard all-purpose road and a slip road (see paras 10.2 to 10.12). It may also be used at the bifurcation or convergence of two motorways or similar roads. The parallel-sided version (diagram 1042.1) is used to indicate a segregated left turn lane (see paras 8.34 to 8.38). The width of the longitudinal lines may be 150 mm when the marking is used between two lanes at a roundabout (see figure 8-5) or on an all-purpose dual carriageway road without hard shoulders. Except at a roundabout, the boundary lines may be replaced with the marking shown in diagram 1012.2 or 1012.3 as appropriate.

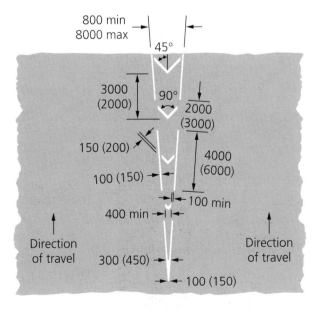

Diagram 1041

Figure 4-17

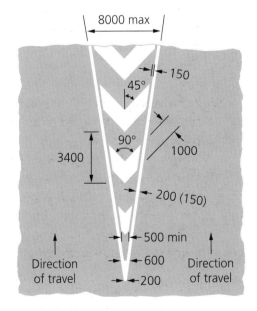

Diagram 1042

Figure 4-18

4.62 The chevrons in all diagrams must always point towards approaching traffic, i.e. in figures 4-17 and 4-18 they should be reversed when traffic is merging. Where road studs are used, these must be coloured red. Clearance between the inside edge of the boundary line and any kerb should be as indicated in para 4.23.

LAYOUT OF MARKINGS BETWEEN JUNCTIONS

4.63 The layout of road markings between junctions on high standard roads designed to TD 9/93 in Volume 6 of the Design Manual for Roads and Bridges (see para 1.4) is shown in figure 4-19 for all-purpose roads and figure 4-20 for motorways (all

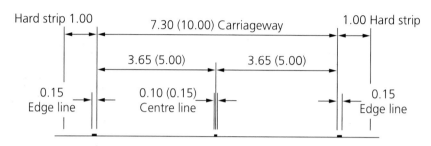

All-purpose single carriageway road

Dimensions in brackets are for a 10 metre wide single carriageway

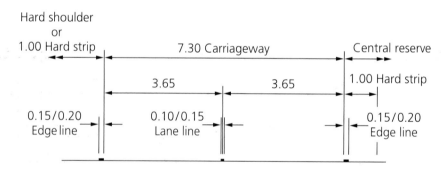

Two-lane all-purpose dual carriageway road

See tables 4-2 and 4-5 for guidance on appropriate line width

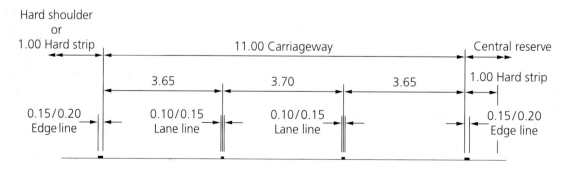

Three-lane all-purpose dual carriageway road

See tables 4-2 and 4-5 for guidance on appropriate line width

Figure 4-19

dimensions are in metres). These illustrate the placing of the lines in relation to the cross section of the road (see TD 27/96 for guidance on marking slip roads).

4.64 Edge of carriageway markings between the running lanes and the hard shoulder or hard strip may use raised rib profiles (diagram 1012.2 on motorways and 1012.3 on all-purpose roads; see paras 4.39 to 4.48 for details).

4.65 Edge lines should be accompanied by red uni-directional retroreflecting road studs adjacent to the hard shoulder or near side hard strip and, on motorways and dual carriageway roads, coloured amber adjacent to the central reservation. For use during contra-flow working, the amber studs may have red reflectors on the opposite face. The use of road studs in conjunction with road markings is dealt with in more detail in section 6.

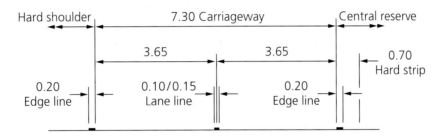

Dual two-lane motorway

See table 4-2 for guidance on appropriate line width

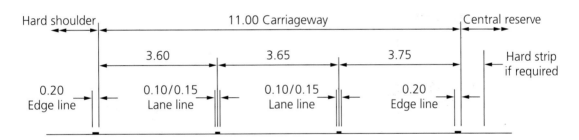

Dual three-lane motorway

See table 4-2 for guidance on appropriate line width

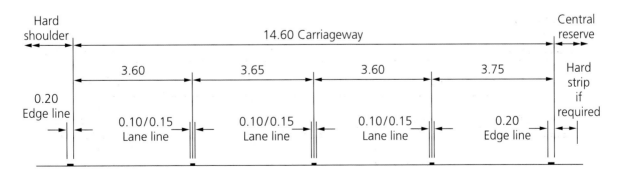

Dual four-lane motorway

See table 4-2 for guidance on appropriate line width

Figure 4-20

5 DOUBLE WHITE LINES

5.1 Double white lines (see figure 5-1) are used to prohibit overtaking where visibility is restricted. Drivers may cross the line nearer to them when it is broken, but not when it is continuous. The legal requirements conveyed by the markings are specified in regulation 26(2) of the Traffic Signs Regulations and General Directions 2002 as follows:

    (a) no vehicle shall stop on any length of road along which the marking has been placed at any point between the ends of the marking, and

    (b) every vehicle proceeding on any length of road along which the marking has been so placed that, as viewed in the direction of travel of the vehicle, a continuous line is on the left of a broken line or of another continuous line, shall be so driven as to keep the first-mentioned continuous line on the right hand or off side of the vehicle.

Exceptions are set out in regulations 26(4), 26(5) and 26(6), which list the circumstances in which vehicles are permitted to stop on a road marked with double white lines and the occasions when vehicles may cross a continuous line. The restriction on stopping in (a) above applies whether the line closest to the vehicle is continuous or broken. However, on a road with more than one traffic lane in each direction the stopping restriction does not apply. A separate traffic regulation order would therefore be necessary to prohibit waiting or loading on, for example, an urban four-lane road (see para 5.26).

5.2 Each direction of travel is marked separately according to the degree of visibility in that direction. The necessary standard of visibility is governed by the speed of vehicles on the road; surveys carried out in the summer and winter months may produce differing visibility as a result of foliage growth. Where visibility is just above the minimum standard, but overtaking may nevertheless present a danger, the warning line to diagram 1004 or 1004.1 should be used (see para 4.4). A "no overtaking" order may be imposed (see Chapter 3), but this is likely to be necessary only in very exceptional circumstances.

5.3 A continuous length of double white lines, with any number of changes between continuous and broken lines in either direction, comprises a system. A double white line scheme may comprise any number of separate systems, interrupted by other types of marking (e.g. centre lines or warning lines).

5.4 Having regard to the road width required by buses and goods vehicles, particularly on bends, double line markings should not normally be used where the carriageway is less than 6.1 m wide; a warning line should be used instead. However, an exception may be made where the width of a road drops marginally below 6.1 m for a short distance, and the omission of double lines at places of restricted visibility within the narrow section might be misleading.

5.5 Where the forward visibility is less than the desirable minimum (see para 5.22) it does not automatically follow that double lines should always be installed; judgement should be exercised in deciding whether, having regard to the topographical and traffic characteristics of the route, it is reasonable to impose the restrictions or whether the warning type of marking should be used instead. Double white lines are in general well respected, but they impose arbitrary restrictions on some drivers - for example those who have a better view because they are seated higher above the road. It is important that the marking is not used where the appropriate criteria are not satisfied, otherwise it will be brought into disrepute and eventually lose the respect of drivers. Routes, including those that cross traffic authority boundaries, should be considered as a whole, in order to maintain consistent standards.

5.6 Traffic authorities should ensure that all newly-laid double line markings conform to the criteria set out in the following paragraphs. The emphasis should always be on not using double lines except where they are clearly justified on these criteria, in relation to both the length in question and as part of the route as a whole.

5.7 It is not necessary to obtain formal authorisation for the lines because discretion in deciding whether to use double lines or warning lines is left to traffic authorities. However, as contravention of the prohibitory line is an endorsable offence and is subject to the "totting-up" procedure (section 36 of the Road Traffic Act 1988) the appropriate Commissioner of Police or Chief Constable should always be consulted whenever it is proposed to install new double line markings.

5.8 Double lines should not normally be used in built-up areas, as preventing vehicles from stopping could be unduly restrictive. They might, however, be required at certain difficult positions, on three-lane hills (see para 5.27 to 5.35) or at level crossings (see paras 19.13 to 19.17).

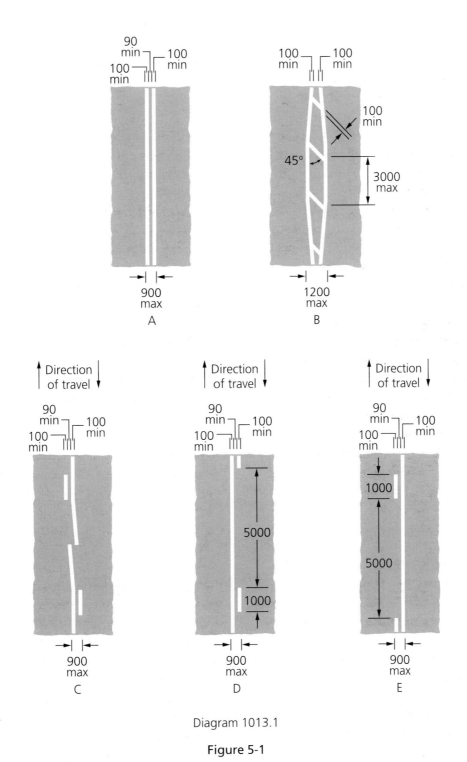

Diagram 1013.1

Figure 5-1

DESCRIPTION

5.9 Double lines consist of a continuous prohibitory line accompanied either by another continuous line or by a broken permissive line to provide for the different forward visibilities in opposite directions. The broken line comprises 1 m marks with 5 m gaps. The two lines are normally spaced 175 mm apart (minimum 90 mm). The Regulations require each line to be a minimum of 100 mm wide, but 150 mm should normally be used. The overall maximum width of both lines and the gap between them must not exceed 900 mm. If a wider marking is required, version B prescribed in diagram 1013.1 (see figure 5-1) may be used, with a maximum overall width of 1200 mm. The version B marking usually tapers at each end to connect with version A, but may abut diagram 1040.2.

5.10 All double white lines must be laid in reflectorised material (regulation 31). Raised rib markings (see paras 4.39 to 4.48) must not be used. When laid in the nominal centre of the carriageway, they should be placed either symmetrically about the centre line or with the continuous line along the centre. The former arrangement would make a new installation cheaper when road studs (particularly the depressible type) are already in use. However, if the road is narrow, the latter layout could be used to give extra width to the side with the prohibitory line (see also para 5.4).

ROAD STUDS

5.11 Regulation 31(3) requires double white line systems to be fitted with road studs. Except in the circumstances detailed in para 5.12, a single row of bi-directional reflecting road studs is placed between the lines at centres between 3 m and 4.5 m. Other than at level crossings, where a spacing of 4 m should be used (see para 19.16), it is recommended that a 4.5 m spacing is adopted on all new installations. Provided they are within the above range of dimensions, it is not necessary to change existing installations to 4.5 m spacing merely to comply with this paragraph.

5.12 Where the road marking shown in version B of diagram 1013.1 is so placed that the continuous lines are more than 175 mm apart and separated by the cross-hatching shown, the studs may be fitted in opposite pairs, within the width of each of the two lines, as an alternative to a single row between them (regulation 31(4)). When they are fitted in pairs, studs should be uni-directional so that only the line of studs nearer to the driver is fitted with reflectors which can be seen by that driver.

DEFLECTION ARROWS

5.13 Direction 48 requires the provision of at least one arrow to diagram 1014 (see figure 13-6) in advance of the start of any continuous line which is on the driver's side, to warn of the approaching restriction (see also paras 5.16 and 5.18). If space permits, two arrows should normally be provided. Where a driver's forward view of the road surface is limited, as at a crest, a third arrow may be necessary to give adequate forewarning (see figure 5-2).

5.14 Deflection arrows on the approach to a double white line system (see para 5.3) are usually positioned in the centre of the carriageway (see figure 5-2) replacing one of the centre line marks. Where the centre is marked using diagram 1040.2, the omission of a pair of edge marks and the associated diagonals will emphasise the arrow. Where arrows are required within a double white line system, they should be positioned approximately 500 mm to the right of the continuous line in order to avoid breaking the double white line pattern (see figure 5-3). All arrows on each approach must be in line with one another.

5.15 The first arrow should normally be placed a distance in advance of the start of a continuous line equivalent to one second of travel, the second arrow at a point equivalent to a further two seconds of travel, and the third, where necessary, at a point equivalent to a distance of a further three seconds of travel. The spacing for various speeds given in table 5-1 has been adjusted to fit the standard modules so that the arrow is positioned equidistantly between two warning marks.

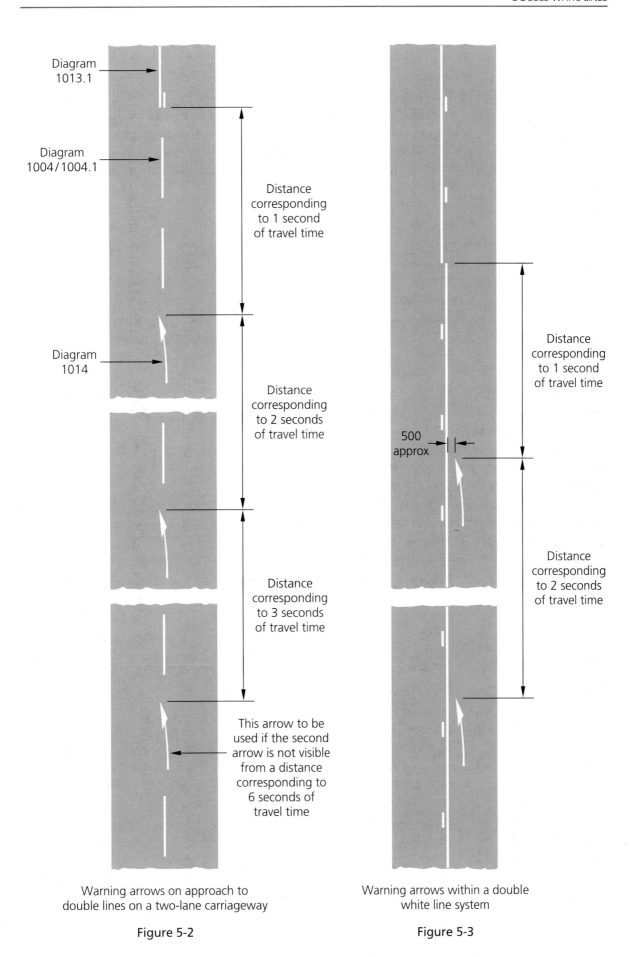

Diagram
1013.1

Diagram
1004/1004.1

Diagram
1014

Distance
corresponding
to 1 second
of travel time

Distance
corresponding
to 2 seconds
of travel time

Distance
corresponding
to 3 seconds
of travel time

This arrow to be
used if the second
arrow is not visible
from a distance
corresponding to
6 seconds of
travel time

Distance
corresponding
to 1 second
of travel time

500
approx

Distance
corresponding
to 2 seconds
of travel time

Warning arrows on approach to
double lines on a two-lane carriageway

Figure 5-2

Warning arrows within a double
white line system

Figure 5-3

5.16 Direction 48 provides an exemption to the requirement for deflection arrows where the continuous line is interrupted at a junction or at a refuge (see also para 7.11). They are also not required if a continuous line commences immediately after the point where a central reservation ends, or immediately after a roundabout. However, in the latter case the use of an arrow is recommended, as indicated in figure 5-4.

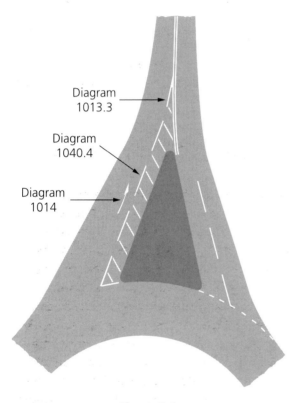

Diagram 1013.3

Diagram 1040.4

Diagram 1014

Figure 5-4

SPLAYED MARKINGS ON BENDS AND CRESTS

5.17 To increase the lateral separation of opposing traffic on sharp bends or crests, double continuous lines, where they are justified, may be splayed with a maximum overall width of 1200 mm (diagram 1013.1 version B); if greater widths are required, diagram 1013.4 should be used (see figures 7.5 and 7.6). It is essential that there is adequate room on each side to enable vehicles to negotiate the bend or hump without crossing the lines. The lines should be opened out at a taper no sharper than 1 in 50; the area between them must be hatched with marks of the same width as the longitudinal lines, at spacings of not more than 3 m. On a crest, the lines should attain maximum width at the point of least visibility (not always the highest point) in each direction. This hatched marking may be used only between double continuous lines, never between a continuous and a broken line.

INCLINED LINES AT REFUGES

5.18 Double lines should not be splayed where they meet a refuge. Both lines should be inclined to the driver's side of the refuge, keeping them parallel to each other so that traffic is guided safely past the refuge (see figure 5-5). Guidance on the appropriate offset between the line and the refuge can be found in para 4.23. Lines should not be continued alongside the refuge. Recommended tapers are set out in table 14-1. Where a refuge interrupts a continuous line, warning arrows are not required at the recommencement of the marking after the refuge. If on the approach to a refuge the line on the driver's

Table 5-1 Location of deflection arrows

Speed limit (mph)	Length of arrow (m)	Distance of tip of arrow from the start of the unbroken line (m)		
		First arrow	Second arrow	Third arrow
30	4.5	13.75	43.75	79.75
40	4.5	19.75	55.75	109.75
50	6	21.00	66.00	138.00
60	6	30.00	84.00	165.00

side is broken, it should be replaced with a continuous line between the refuge and a point V metres in advance of it (see table 5-2). This avoids inviting an unsafe overtaking manoeuvre.

ROAD JUNCTIONS

5.19 Improved visibility sometimes results in reversion to a broken line on the approach to a junction. In such cases, it is better to maintain the continuous line beyond the junction to avoid encouraging overtaking at an unsuitable point.

5.20 The Regulations permit vehicles to cross the continuous line to enter any other road or private access (regulation 26(6)). A gap in the line is not therefore necessary. However, where there is a dedicated right turn lane this should be marked out as shown in figure 7-4 and described in para 7.11. The Directions do not require deflection arrows at the recommencement of the double line either side of the junction.

5.21 The use of double white lines in conjunction with a right turn lane on a road with a climbing lane is dealt with in para 7.12.

VISIBILITY DISTANCE

5.22 Visibility distance is defined as the maximum distance at which an object 1.05 m above the carriageway can be seen by an observer at the same height, taking account of vertical as well as horizontal curvature. In table 5-2, for each speed interval, V is the desirable minimum visibility distance and W is the warning line visibility distance as measured between points on the centre of the carriageway. Warning lines are laid where overtaking

Table 5-2 Visibility distance

85 percentile speed (mph)	Desirable minimum visibility distance V (m)	Warning line visibility distance W (m)
Up to 30	75	115
31 to 40	95	160
41 to 50	120	195
51 to 60	150	240
Over 60	175	275

is potentially hazardous, but visibility is not so restricted that overtaking needs to be prohibited (see paras 4.12 to 4.26).

DESIGN PROCEDURE FOR TWO-LANE ROADS

5.23 Double white line systems (see para 5.3) should not be designed entirely on the basis of plans and sight distance data. A site visit should always be made, and other relevant information such as the accident record taken into account. The complete scheme, with all adjustments, deflection arrows and associated markings should then be designed on a large-scale plan before any markings are laid on the road. The visibility distances used to determine the double line scheme should be based on actual 85th percentile measured speeds where this is higher than the speed limit. For measured 85th percentile speeds of 30 mph or less (see table 5-2) the visibility distances for 30 mph should be used.

Step 1   Determine traffic speeds along the section for each direction of travel. From table 5-2, find the desirable minimum visibility V for each part of the section, in each direction.

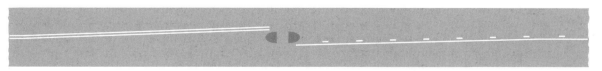

For angle of taper see table 14-1

Figure 5-5

Step 2   For one direction of travel, mark each of the points where desirable minimum visibility distance V is lost, and where it is regained. Each of these pairs of points can now be joined by a continuous white line to create a series of line segments, except where such a segment would be shorter than V/4, and would be separated from its preceding and succeeding segments by at least the relevant V (note 1(a) below); such short isolated segments should not be marked as continuous unless there is very good justification for retaining them.

Step 3   On the exit from a left hand bend, the continuous line should be extended until the warning line visibility distance W is attained, or the road ceases to curve to the left, whichever results in the shorter line.

Step 4   Gaps shorter than the relevant V (note 1(a)) between continuous line segments should be closed by extending the continuous line.

Step 5   Repeat Steps 2, 3 and 4 for the other direction of travel.

Step 6   On the plan, mark broken lines alongside remaining single continuous lines, on the appropriate side (i.e. on the side for the direction of travel in which a driver has visibility better than V). This will result in the creation of a number of lengths of double white lines.

Step 7   If the gap between two lengths of double white line systems is shorter than half the relevant V value (notes 1(b) and 2 below), the systems should be extended, without a change in pattern, to fill the gap. Normally the systems would meet in the middle of the gap, but the designer should adjust the point of meeting to minimise loss of length from overtaking sections (note 3), or to avoid the release of traffic at an unsuitable point.

Step 8   If this joining of systems results in a length of broken line within the resulting system (i.e. not at one end) that is shorter than the relevant V (note 1(a)), then that length of broken line should be replaced by a continuous line.

Step 9   If the gap between two systems is greater than half the relevant V (note 1(b)), but less than the relevant W (note 4), warning lines should be laid in the gap between the systems.

Step 10 If traffic leaving a length of double white lines is subject to a continuous line that extends beyond the point where the continuous line for traffic in the other direction starts, and it seems that this might cause confusion, the inbound continuous line may be started sooner, at the designer's discretion.

NOTES:

1(a) In a particular direction, the relevant V value for a gap between two continuous lines is taken to be the same as that used to determine the start of the continuous line after the gap.
 (b) When considering the gap between two systems, if the application of note 1(a) results in a different V in each direction, the greater value should be used.
2   V/2 is used here in preference to V to avoid excessive lengths of unnecessary continuous line. Overtaking lengths less than V that might arise are closed later, at Step 8.
3   When adjusting the meeting point of systems, the designer should take account of the availability of other (perhaps safer) overtaking opportunities in the vicinity.
4   The relevant W value at any point is taken to be that for the speed corresponding to the relevant V value at that point, defined under 1(a) and 1(b) above.

5.24 The above procedure achieves the following:

    (i)   the minimum length for an overtaking stretch is V,

    (ii)   the minimum length for a broken line element within a system is V, and

    (iii) the minimum length for a stretch of warning line between two systems is V/2.

This minimises both frequent changes of pattern and the length of continuous line put down at places where visibility is adequate.

THREE-LANE ROADS

5.25 The use of offset double lines on alternate sections of three-lane roads (other than three-lane hills, see paras 5.27 to 5.32) to facilitate overtaking in the centre lane is not recommended. Drivers will not respect restrictions which have no apparent justification. Carriageways 10 m or more in width may be marked with a centre of carriageway marking in accordance with table 4-3, or with double white lines if there are four or more lanes (see para 5.26).

FOUR-LANE ROADS

5.26 On single carriageway roads with two or more lanes in each direction, the centre may be marked with a double continuous line irrespective of visibility. This should eliminate the possibility of a vehicle overtaking in one direction being confronted by an opposing vehicle which is "double overtaking" by crossing the centre line.

THREE-LANE HILLS

5.27 A three-lane hill is intended to provide two lanes for ascending traffic so that faster-moving vehicles may overtake slower ones in safety. The downhill traffic may be fully confined to one lane, or partially confined if overtaking is permitted. The left hand uphill lane should be a continuation of the near side lane, with the widening to the right, so that

slower vehicles do not have to change lanes at either end. The procedure for marking three-lane hills, set out below, is designed to result in markings that allow downhill overtaking only at those locations where visibility is extensive in both directions.

5.28 A three-lane hill is marked with a lane line (diagram 1005 or 1005.1) separating the two uphill lanes, and a double white line separating them from the downhill lane (see figure 5-6). Where the carriageway width is the standard 10 m (excluding any edge strips) it should be marked so that the uphill climbing lane is 3.2 m wide and the other lanes each 3.4 m wide. For further details see TD 9/93 in the Design Manual for Roads and Bridges (Volume 6).

5.29 The double white line will always feature a continuous line on the side of the uphill traffic. On the downhill side, where certain criteria are met, the line may be broken to permit overtaking. These criteria are determined as follows:

    (i)   establish the 85th percentile traffic speed for the downhill direction, and determine from table 5-2 the appropriate warning line visibility distance W,

    (ii)   measure downhill visibility with the observer on the proposed alignment of the double white line, but with two targets, one on the proposed alignment, and the other on the lane line separating the two uphill lanes. The visibility criteria are satisfied only when both targets are simultaneously visible at a distance W from the observer, and when no part of the sight line to the target on the lane line at any point passes over the inside uphill lane (where it could be obscured by an uphill vehicle). This ensures adequate forward vision for a driver in either direction who intends using the centre lane to overtake,

    (iii) a broken line is installed for downhill traffic only where the criteria in Step 2 of para 5.23 are satisfied, and only if it can be installed for a minimum length W. Otherwise a continuous line is used to prohibit downhill overtaking.

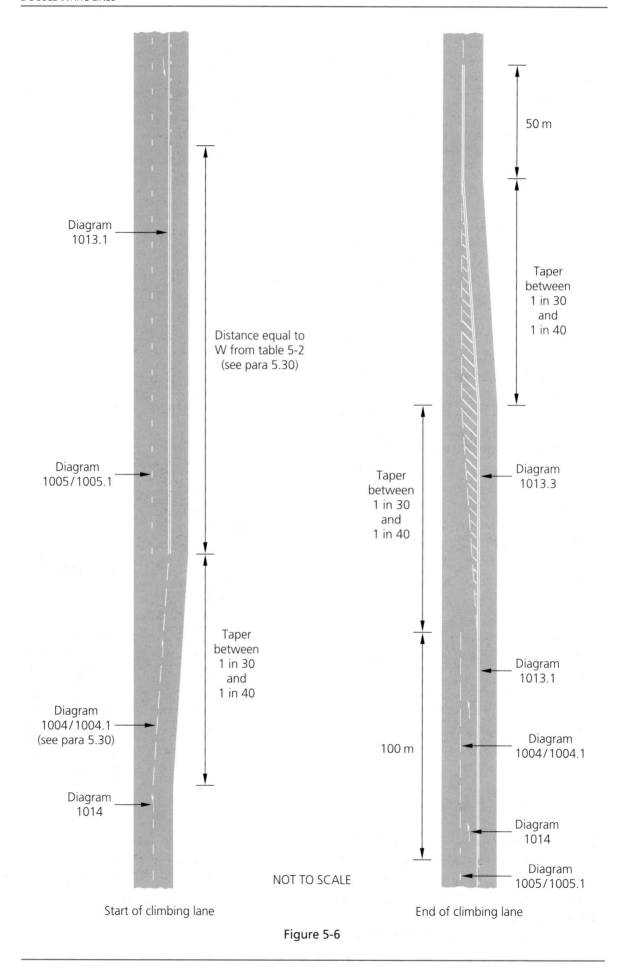

Diagram 1013.1

Diagram 1005/1005.1

Distance equal to W from table 5-2 (see para 5.30)

Diagram 1004/1004.1 (see para 5.30)

Diagram 1014

Taper between 1 in 30 and 1 in 40

50 m

Taper between 1 in 30 and 1 in 40

Diagram 1013.3

Taper between 1 in 30 and 1 in 40

Diagram 1013.1

100 m

Diagram 1004/1004.1

Diagram 1014

Diagram 1005/1005.1

NOT TO SCALE

Start of climbing lane

End of climbing lane

Figure 5-6

38

To avoid frequent changes of pattern on long hills, or for safety reasons, the designer may on occasion use a downhill continuous line even when the visibility criteria for a broken line in Step 2 are satisfied, although the use of a prohibitory line on long straight sections should be avoided if possible.

5.30 The marking at the commencement of the climbing lane is designed to encourage uphill drivers to keep to the near side lane unless overtaking. In order to avoid a potential conflict at this point between uphill and downhill overtaking traffic, a length of double continuous line should be provided for a length equal to W in table 5-2 for the speed of the uphill traffic. This ensures that any downhill overtaking vehicle will be returned to the near side lane before coming into conflict with an uphill vehicle beginning an overtaking manoeuvre at the start of the climbing lane (see figure 5-6). In addition, the double white line may be extended to divide opposing traffic over the taper in order to prevent overtaking by downhill traffic. However, if visibility over this length is good, then observance may be poor and a warning line might be more effective.

5.31 This procedure will still allow downhill overtaking on long straight, or nearly straight, hills. It will restrict it elsewhere, particularly in those cases where visibility is poor for an uphill inside lane vehicle trying to pull out from behind a large vehicle.

5.32 The alignment at the end of a climbing lane should place the onus on the overtaking driver to rejoin the inside lane. Care should be taken to ensure that the return to a single lane does not occur where junctions or sharp curves may cause problems. See figure 5-6 for the layout of markings at the top and bottom of a climbing lane. Signs to diagram 517 should also be used (see Chapter 4, para 4.3).

LAYOUT AT SAG CURVES

5.33 Where there are climbing lanes on both sides of a sag curve, a conventional two-lane road layout may be used to link them, provided this is at least 500 m in length between tapers. For shorter lengths, the intervening carriageway should be maintained at 10 m wide and the climbing lanes extended

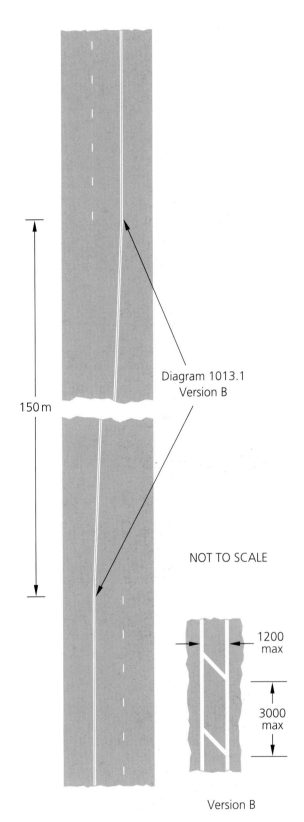

150 m

Diagram 1013.1
Version B

NOT TO SCALE

1200 max

3000 max

Version B

Layout of markings at sag
between two climbing lanes

Figure 5-7

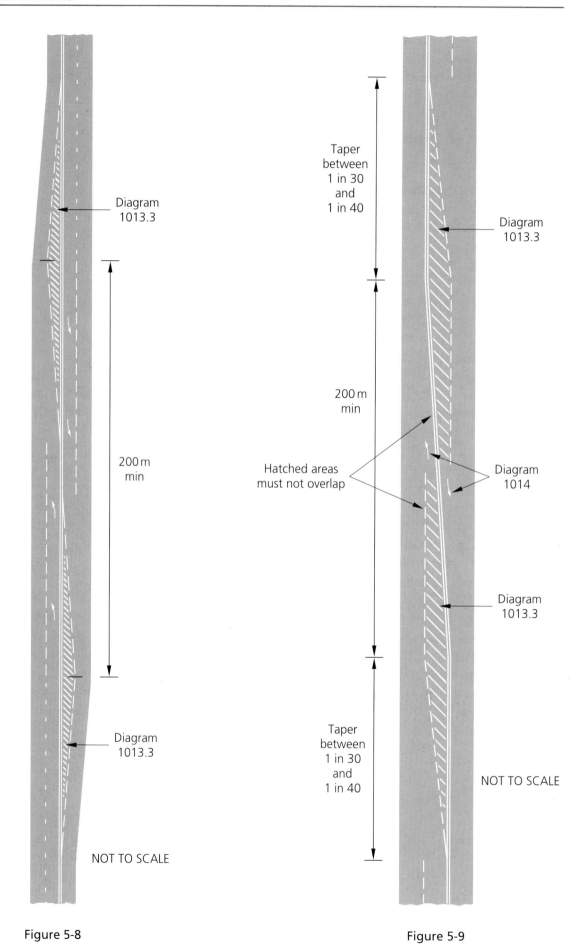

Figure 5-8

Figure 5-9

downhill until they meet, using a road marking to diagram 1013.1 version B (see figure 5-7). The taper in the version B marking (see figure 5-1) should not be sharper than 1 in 50.

LAYOUT AT CRESTS

5.34 Where there are climbing lanes on both sides of the hill and the road has been widened on the crest to 13.2 m, as indicated in TD 9/93 (Amendment No. 1) in Volume 6 of the Design Manual for Roads and Bridges (see para 1.4) then:

(i)   if the length of 13.2 m wide carriageway (including any hatched area) between the tapers is 500 m or more, a conventional layout should be used between the tapers,

(ii) if the length of 13.2 m wide carriageway between the tapers is less than 500 m, the climbing lanes should overlap as shown in figure 5-8. In this case the distance between the tapers (i.e. the length of 13.2 m carriageway including hatching) should not be less than 200 m.

5.35 If the carriageway over the crest remains unchanged in width at 10 m, the marking layout shown in figure 5-9 should be adopted.

LEVEL CROSSINGS

5.36 Double white lines are used at some level crossings even when the conditions do not meet the visibility criteria in table 5-2 (see paras 19.9 to 19.17 for details). Markings should be installed at level crossings only after consultation with HM Railway Inspectorate.

6 ROAD STUDS

GENERAL

6.1 Retroreflective road studs are frequently used to supplement longitudinal road markings. They depend for their brightness on the light from a vehicle's headlamps being reflected back towards the source. The driver sits behind the headlamps and sees a bright reflection from the stud. They are used in addition to reflectorised lines where traffic flows are high, particularly on roads without street lighting. They remain effective in wet weather and also in areas prone to fog, when the efficiency of reflective markings is reduced.

6.2 Regulations 31(3) and (7) require white road studs to be used in conjunction with the double white line system (diagrams 1013.1, 1013.3 and 1013.4). They are usually placed in a single row between the lines, but regulation 31(4) permits a double row in certain circumstances (see paras 5.11 and 5.12).

6.3 Road studs may be used with most other longitudinal white lines (see direction 31(5), (6) and (7)). They are always used on motorways, and are recommended for use on high speed all-purpose roads, even when street lighting is provided.

6.4 For guidance on the use of road studs at the change from dual to single carriageway, see paras 4.58 and 4.59. The positioning of studs relative to edge lines is dealt with in para 4.38.

6.5 Bi-directional road studs may be used for certain applications on single carriageway roads, including the double white lines in diagrams 1013.1,1013.3 and 1013.4 (subject to the exception described in para 5.12), and should always be used in a line that separates opposing flows of traffic. They are not appropriate for marking lines bounding central hatched markings; these should make use of the uni-directional type. This is because bi-directional studs can make the hatched area appear to be another traffic lane, especially on wet roads at night, when the hatched markings may not be clearly visible. Moreover, because reflectors on the leading edge of a bi-directional stud tend to deteriorate faster than those on the trailing edge, it can also result in the studs on the far side of the hatching or taper being brighter than those on the nearer side. There is then a risk of drivers being guided onto the hatched area.

TYPE APPROVAL

6.6 BS 873: Part 4 has been replaced by the European Standard BS EN 1463, and the former type approval process under which studs had to be approved by the Secretary of State has been superseded. Type approval will continue to be needed for studs outside the scope of the European Standard, e.g. those which incorporate a light source. The minimum performance requirement for retroreflective road studs is now specified in direction 57 by reference to the appropriate classes set out in parts 1 and 2 of BS EN 1463.

TYPES OF ROAD STUD

6.7 Studs may be permanent or temporary, and use a glass or plastic reflector, or a plastic reflector with an abrasion resistant protective coating. The standard provides several different photometric performance classes, depending on the stud type.

6.8 Studs may also be depressible or non-depressible. In the former, the stud is mounted in a base unit which is embedded into the carriageway. It is designed in such a way that a passing vehicle depresses the stud thus wiping the reflectors clean by a "squeegee" action. Non-depressible studs with rigid retroreflectors can be surface bonded or anchored using suitable adhesives, or embedded into the carriageway using a base unit. The maximum prescribed height for a depressible stud is 25 mm and for a non-depressible stud 20 mm (regulation 32).

COLOUR OF ROAD STUDS

6.9 Retroreflecting road studs are prescribed for use with reflectors coloured white, red, amber or green (regulation 31(7)). The colours are specified by chromaticity co-ordinates in BS EN 1463-1 and are used as follows:

WHITE - to indicate a traffic lane or centre of carriageway marking.

RED - to indicate a line of studs which should not be crossed. It is used mainly to delineate the left hand edge of the running carriageway; studs are omitted at positions where traffic is permitted to cross, e.g. at lay-bys (where green studs are normally substituted). Where studs are used with chevron markings to diagram 1041, 1041.1, 1042 or 1042.1 they must be coloured red on both sides of the marking.

AMBER- to indicate a line of studs which should not be crossed. It is used to indicate the right hand edge of the running carriageway adjacent to the edge of the central reservation or to traffic cones or cylinders at road works, or the marking to diagram 1040.3. Amber studs are also used on the off side of a one-way road (including one-way slip roads and link roads).

GREEN - to indicate a length of the edge of the carriageway which may be crossed. Green studs are used with markings to diagram 1010 (see paras 4.29 and 4.30) at lay-bys and to mark the boundary of acceleration and deceleration lanes on the left hand side of the carriageway. They must not be used in conjunction with Stop or Give Way transverse markings, or with diagram 1009. At lane-drop junctions, and right turn lanes, (see figure 7-7) green studs are used with the marking to diagram 1010 which demarcates the exit lane.

6.10 On dual carriageway roads, amber studs placed adjacent to the central reservation may have red reflectors on the reverse for use when contra-flow working is needed for road maintenance purposes.

6.11 The colour of the road stud body may be:

(i) white,

(ii) the same as the reflectors or retroreflecting material,

(iii) a natural metallic finish, or

(iv) any other neutral colour (including black).

In the case of studs placed temporarily at road works, the stud body must be fluorescent green/yellow. The use of temporary studs is described in Chapter 8.

STUD SPACING

6.12 The spacing of road studs used with double white lines is dealt with in para 5.11. The spacing of studs used with centre lines and lane lines is described in tables 4-1, 4-2 and 4-3, and studs used in conjunction with continuous edge lines or with diagram 1010 in table 4-5 and para 10.11.

6.13 On dual carriageway roads where red, white and amber studs are used, these are normally spaced at 18 m intervals. There may be some minor advantage in offsetting the white lane line studs 9 m longitudinally relative to the red and amber studs. Where red studs are used adjacent to chevron markings, the spacing should be closed up to 3 m centres.

6.14 The standard 18 m spacing should be reduced to 9 m on bends with a radius of curvature less than 450 m, or on roads particularly prone to fog and mist or where there is a severe dazzle problem caused by glare from the headlamps of oncoming vehicles.

ROAD STUDS AT CROSSINGS

6.15 Road studs to diagram 1055.1 or 1055.2 used to mark a crossing place must be coloured white, silver or light grey (regulation 11(4)). They may not be fitted with reflective lenses or with a steady or intermittent light source, but may be formed from retroreflecting material. Although the Regulations permit the use of stainless steel, aluminium, thermoplastic or paint products, some types of metal studs can be slippery when wet, and the potential risk to two-wheeled traffic should be borne in mind. Similar considerations apply to the studs used at other types of pedestrian crossing.

7 MAJOR / MINOR JUNCTIONS

SIMPLE JUNCTIONS

7.1 Figure 7-1 illustrates the layout of simple T-junctions. Guidance on the use of Give Way lines (diagram 1003) can be found in paras 3.14 to 3.23, on warning lines (diagrams 1004/1004.1) in paras 4.12 to 4.26 and on edge lines (diagrams 1009 and 1010) in paras 4.28 to 4.30. Table 7-1 gives details of the warning line, road studs and the minimum number of marks to be used where practicable. This number may not always be achievable on the minor road if this is narrow.

GHOST ISLAND JUNCTIONS

7.2 Ghost island junctions are usually provided to afford right-turning vehicles some protection and assist free flow of major road through traffic.

7.3 The use of ghost islands on unrestricted rural single carriageway roads can sometimes pose safety problems. Where overtaking opportunities on the major road are limited, the presence of a widened carriageway, albeit with hatched markings, might result in overtaking manoeuvres which conflict with right turns into and out of the minor road. Where this proves to be a problem, consideration should be given to the use of kerbed islands to prevent overtaking and to guide traffic through the junction. Alternatively, double white lines as described in paras 7.11 and 7.12 may be used.

7.4 The through lane in each direction ((c) in figure 7-2) should not be more than 3.65 m wide, exclusive of hard strips, nor less than 3 m. The desirable width of the turning lane (d) is 3.5 m, although this may be reduced to 3 m (but see para 7.5). At urban junctions it can sometimes be advantageous to use a wider turning lane, not exceeding 5 m. This provides some degree of shelter in the centre of the road, helping vehicles turning right from the minor road to make the turn in two separate stages. On rural roads, with speeds above 85 kph (50 mph), or where hard strips are present, widths greater than 3.65 m are inadvisable because wide ghost islands in these situations create a sense of space which could encourage overtaking at hazardous locations. Where space is very limited, a reduced width may be unavoidable. In such cases the width of ghost islands should not be less than 2.5 m, except as described in para 7.5.

7.5 On narrow urban roads it might not be possible to provide full width right-turning lanes. It might still be worth offsetting the main road centre line towards the minor road and using hatched markings to diagram 1040, even if the hatched width is less than 2.5 m. This can create space to help ahead traffic pass right-turning vehicles and make the junction more conspicuous. However, this technique is not appropriate where the speed limit is more than 30 mph, or the carriageway is less than 7.3 m wide. No through lane should be narrower than 3 m.

Table 7-1 Warning lines at major/minor junctions on single carriageway roads

Diag No.	Speed limit (mph)	Mark (m)	Gap (m)	Width (mm)	Spacing of studs if used (m)	Minimum number of marks on each approach		
						Speed limit (mph)		
						Over 40	40	30
1004	40 or less	4	2	100 (see note)	6	-	7	5
1004.1	Over 40	6	3	100 (see note)	9	7	-	-

NOTE: The width should be increased to 150 mm if the road is 10 m or more in width with no ghost island.

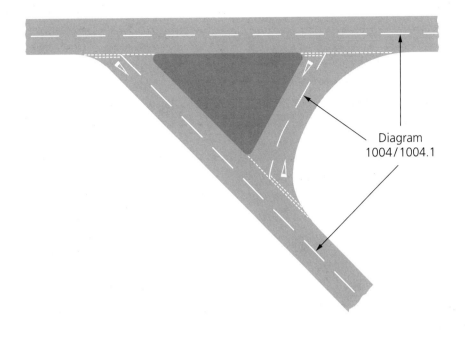

Diagram
1004/1004.1

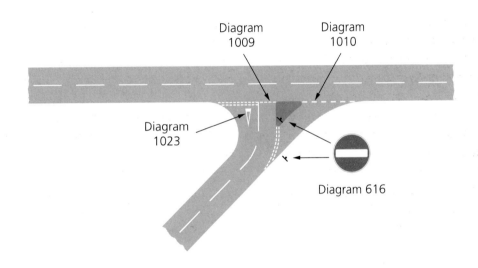

Diagram
1009

Diagram
1010

Diagram
1023

Diagram 616

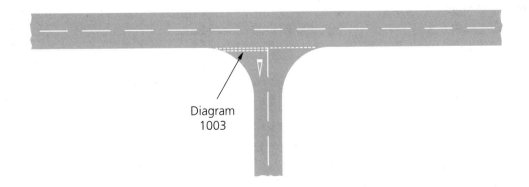

Diagram
1003

Figure 7-1

7.6 Central islands should normally be developed to their maximum width symmetrically about the centre line of the major road using diagram 1040 at the tapers set out in table 7-2.

7.7 The right turn lane is made up of the following elements (see figure 7-2):

(i) turning length (a); this allows long vehicles to position themselves correctly for the right turn. The turning length should be 10 m, measured from the centre line of the minor road irrespective of the type of junction, design speed or gradient. Where capacity calculations indicate that for significant periods of time there will be vehicles queuing to turn right from the major road, the turning length should be increased to allow for a reservoir queuing length to accommodate them. Where this is necessary, consideration should be given to providing physical islands to afford greater protection to turning traffic,

(ii) deceleration length (b); this component of the right turn lane depends upon speed and gradient; its length can be found from table 7-2,

(iii) lane widths (c) and (d) (see para 7.4), and

(iv) direct taper length (e); this is the length over which the width (d) of a right-turning lane is developed. It should be introduced by means of a direct taper which is part of the deceleration length. Its length depends upon the traffic speed and can be found from table 7-2.

7.8 At left/right staggered junctions (see figure 7-3), the deceleration lengths will overlap, but the width of the ghost island should not be increased to accommodate them. The starting points of the right turn lane should be joined by a straight line to diagram 1004 or 1004.1 over the direct taper length (which will be common to both right turn lanes).

7.9 Where the 85th percentile speed is 40 mph or more, two deflection arrows to diagram 1014 (see figure 13-6) should be used on each approach to a ghost island marking; they may also be used where the speed is lower. A third arrow may be used if visibility is limited or if late overtaking is a problem. The spacing depends on the speed limit in the same manner as for double white lines (see para 5.15). The location of arrows in relation to the start of the taper is equivalent to the distances in table 5-1 indicating the position of arrows relative to the start of a continuous white line. The use of deflection arrows in association with double white lines is shown in figures 5-2 and 5-3.

Table 7-2 Ghost island dimensions

85 percentile speed (mph)	Taper either side of centre line	Deceleration length (b) (m)				Direct taper length (e) (m)
		Up gradient		Down gradient		
		0-4%	Over 4%	0-4%	Over 4%	
Up to 30	1 in 40	25	25	25	25	5
31 to 40	1 in 40	30	25	30	50	10
41 to 50	1 in 45	50	35	50	75	15
51 to 60	1 in 50	75	50	75	105	25
61 to 70	1 in 55	100	70	100	135	30

NOTES
a- see para 7.7
b- see table 7-2
c- see para 7.4
d- see para 7.4
e- see para 7.7

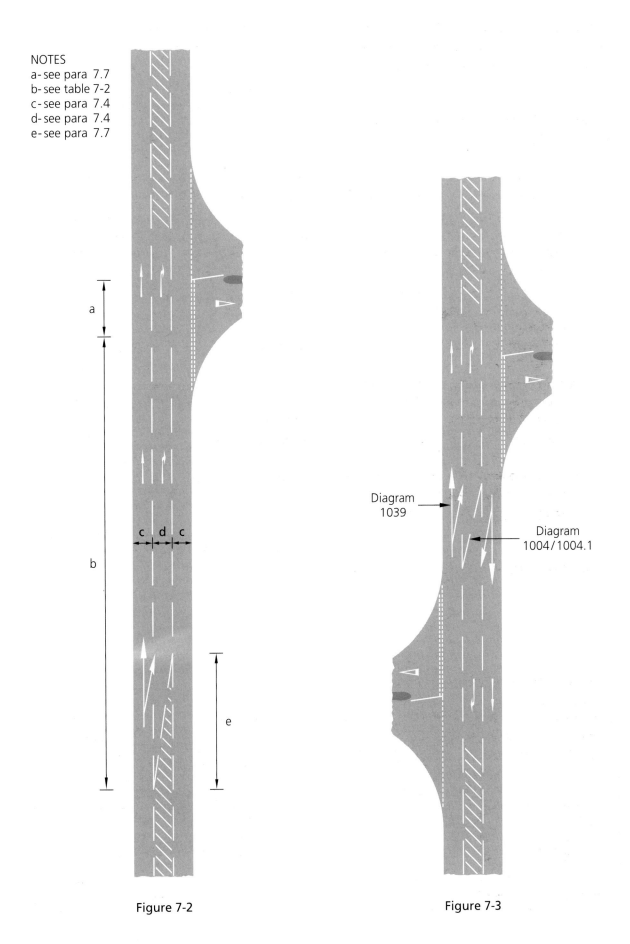

Diagram
1039

Diagram
1004/1004.1

Figure 7-2

Figure 7-3

7.10 Lane indication arrows should be used as follows:

(i)   bifurcation arrow to diagram 1039 at the start of the direct taper length, except where the right turn lane is less than 2.5 m wide (see paras 7.5, 13.10 to 13.14, 14.7 and figure 13-6),

(ii) lane arrows to diagram 1038 (figure 13-1) should be placed as shown in figures 7-2 and 7-3. Except in the case of a short right turn lane for the left/right stagger, at least two arrows per lane should be provided whenever possible, the last being opposite the minor road entry. A right turn arrow should not be used in the ahead lane, as traffic does not turn from that lane. The 4 m arrow should be used for speed limits up to 40 mph and the 6 m arrow for 50 and 60 mph limits.

7.11 To discourage overtaking on the immediate approach to a right turn lane, double white lines may be provided as shown in figure 7-4 using diagrams 1013.1 and 1013.3, even where the usual visibility requirements are not met (but see para 5.7). The maximum width of the former marking is 1200 mm. The lines must not be splayed over a greater width. Unless the visibility criteria are satisfied, the lines should not be extended beyond the immediate area of the junction. Coloured surfacing may be used under the hatched marking to improve conspicuity and discourage encroachment. The Regulations provide an exemption (regulation 26(6)) permitting vehicles to cross the continuous line to enter any other road or private access joining the road along which the line is placed. A gap in the line is therefore not necessary. However, where there is a dedicated right turn lane this should be marked as shown in figure 7-4. Deflection arrows to diagram 1014 are required at the start of the double white line, but not where the double line recommences on either side of the junction (see para 5.16).

7.12 A right turn lane on a road with a climbing lane should be marked as shown in figures 7-5 and 7-6 for uphill and downhill directions respectively. The continuous lines are placed on the side of the

For details of lengths and tapers see figure 7-2

NOT TO SCALE

Figure 7-4

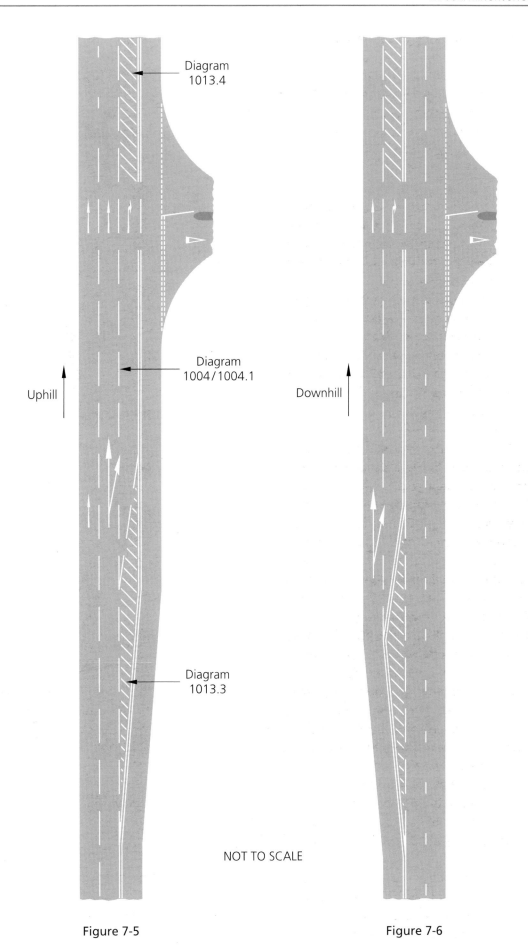

Diagram
1013.4

Diagram
1004 / 1004.1

Uphill

Diagram
1013.3

Downhill

NOT TO SCALE

Figure 7-5

Figure 7-6

hatching that maximises protection for vehicles using the right turn lane, except that where such vehicles are travelling uphill, the continuous lines are on the side that discourages downhill overtaking.

DUAL CARRIAGEWAY JUNCTIONS

7.13 The standard layout for right turns on dual carriageway roads is shown in figure 7-7. The through lanes should maintain their width, and be separated from the right turn lane by a line to diagram 1010, with a width of 100 mm for a speed limit of 40 mph or less, 150 mm for 50 or 60 mph and 200 mm for 70 mph (see table 4-5).

7.14 The lane line through a dual carriageway road junction should be formed of a warning line (to diagram 1004 or 1004.1 as appropriate) in each carriageway as indicated in figure 7-7.

7.15 For guidance on determining the appropriate length of right turn lanes see para 7.7. For details of the markings used at grade separated junctions see section 10.

SINGLE LANE DUALLING

7.16 At single lane dual carriageway junctions (see figure 7-8), the through lane in each direction should be 4.0 m wide, exclusive of hard strips which will normally be 1.0 m wide. Motor vehicles can be discouraged from encroaching onto the hard strips and hatched areas by the use of coloured surfacing as shown in figure 7-8.

7.17 The central reservation opening should be marked to provide a priority arrangement. This should help to reduce uncertainty and discourage parallel queuing of cars in this area.

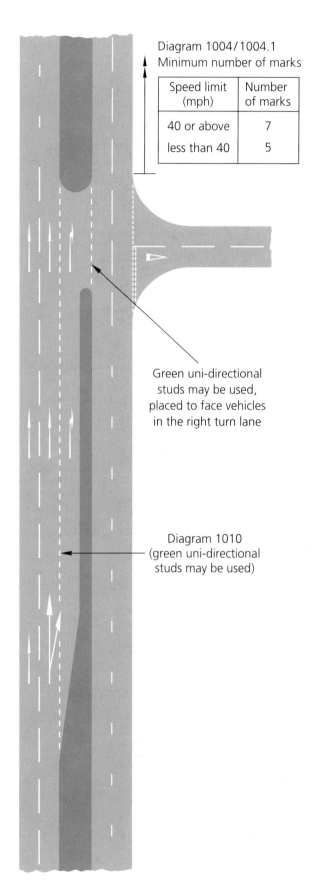

Diagram 1004/1004.1
Minimum number of marks

Speed limit (mph)	Number of marks
40 or above	7
less than 40	5

Green uni-directional studs may be used, placed to face vehicles in the right turn lane

Diagram 1010 (green uni-directional studs may be used)

Figure 7-7

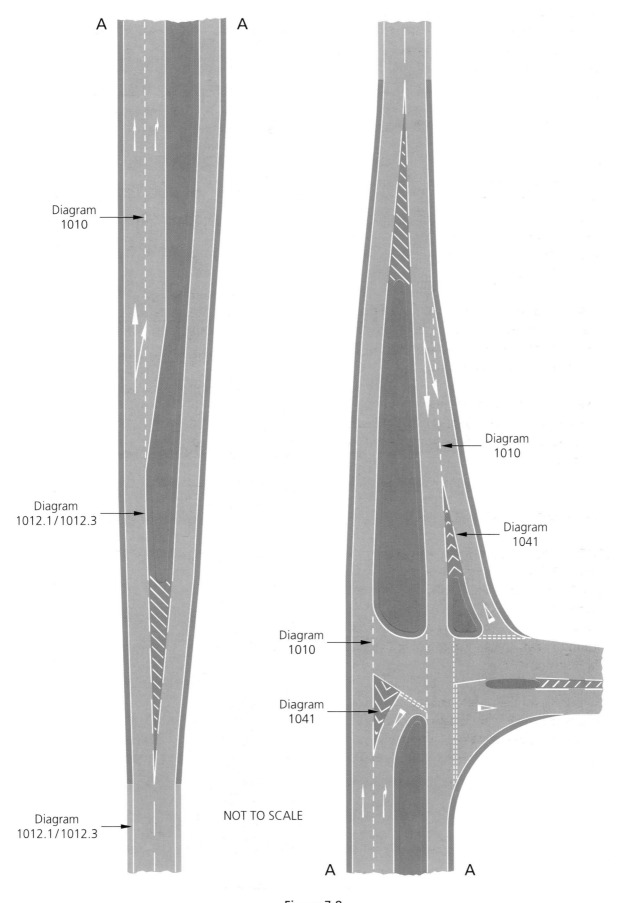

Diagram
1010

Diagram
1012.1/1012.3

Diagram
1012.1/1012.3

Diagram
1010

Diagram
1041

Diagram
1010

Diagram
1041

NOT TO SCALE

Figure 7-8

8 ROUNDABOUTS

GENERAL

8.1 The general rule governing the behaviour of traffic at roundabouts is that drivers should give way to any traffic on their immediate right unless road markings indicate otherwise. This is implemented by the provision of an advisory Give Way line (see paras 8.8 and 8.15) across the entry arm of a roundabout.

8.2 At all roundabouts (except those controlled by traffic signals for 24 hours per day, see paras 8.20 and 8.21) the appropriate prescribed Give Way line should be laid at each entry and should connect the central warning line, deflection island or central reservation to the near side kerb approximately following the line of the inscribed circle. This allows vehicles in the near side lane to be positioned further into the roundabout than those in the off side lane, improving visibility to the right.

8.3 Centre lines and, where provided, lane lines on the approach to roundabouts should be replaced by warning lines (see paras 4.9, 4.24 and table 4-3). Where possible the number of lanes on the approach to the Give Way line should be increased. This will ensure that maximum use is made of gaps in the circulating traffic. However, care should be taken to avoid releasing too much traffic for the space available to receive it. Where the carriageway is widened on the approach to a roundabout and extra lanes provided, drivers should be made aware of this by marking the lanes as early as possible. However, no lane should be less than 2 m wide at the start of the taper, nor less than 3 m wide at the Give Way line (see figure 8-1).

8.4 It is important to provide adequate vehicular deflection through a roundabout to limit vehicle speeds. TD 16/93 in Volume 6 of the Design Manual for Roads and Bridges (see para 1.4) shows how vehicle paths are determined, and how they may be controlled in order to increase deflection.

8.5 The main kinds of roundabouts in use are described as conventional ("normal" in TD 16/93),

mini, double and signalled. These are discussed in the following paragraphs:

(i) conventional roundabout (see paras 8.7 to 8.9),

(ii) mini-roundabout (see paras 8.10 to 8.17),

(iii) double roundabout (see paras 8.18 and 8.19), and

(iv) signalled roundabout (see paras 8.20 and 8.21).

8.6 Other features used include lane markings in the circulating area (see paras 8.22 to 8.29), lane destination markings and arrows (see paras 8.30 to 8.33) and segregated left turn lanes (see paras 8.34 to 8.38).

CONVENTIONAL ROUNDABOUTS

8.7 These have a one-way circulatory carriageway around a kerbed central island, often with flared approaches to allow multiple vehicle entry (see figure 8-1). Physical splitter islands are used to guide traffic and ensure adequate deflection.

8.8 The Give Way marking to diagram 1003.1 is used; the 200 mm wide line at sites where the speed limit is 40 mph or less and the 300 mm size where the limit is greater than 40 mph. The marking to diagram 1003.3 should be adopted when the roundabout has a small central island, up to approximately 4 m in diameter.

8.9 The number of lanes on the approach should be increased where there is room to do so. Extra lanes will increase capacity only if there is sufficient circulating width in the roundabout to accept the traffic and sufficient exit lanes to clear it. Normally it will be the near side lane that widens to provide the extra lane, but widening on the off side provides an extra lane for right-turning traffic.

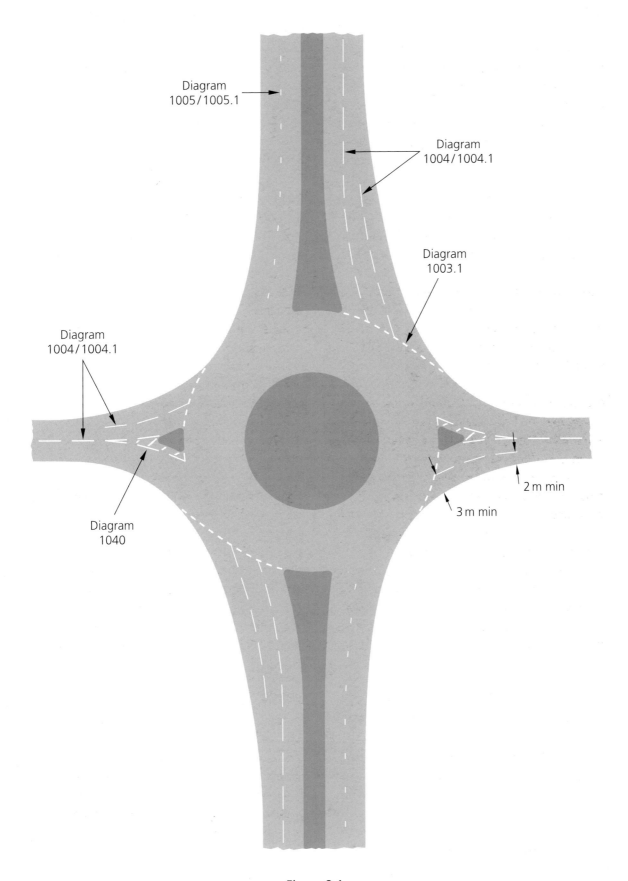

Diagram
1005/1005.1

Diagram
1004/1004.1

Diagram
1003.1

Diagram
1004/1004.1

Diagram
1040

2 m min

3 m min

Figure 8-1

MINI-ROUNDABOUTS

8.10 Mini-roundabouts can be very effective in improving existing urban junctions which experience safety and side road delay problems, and can often be installed with minimal alterations to kerbs etc. They have a one-way circulatory carriageway around a flush or slightly raised central disc, with or without flared approaches. Three arrows around the central disc indicate the direction of circulation. The marking (diagram 1003.4) carries no street furniture, and may be overrun by large vehicles if necessary.

8.11 The layout should be designed so that drivers are made aware in good time that they are approaching a roundabout. Mini-roundabouts should be used only when all approaches are subject to a speed limit of 30 mph or less. Their use on roads with a higher speed limit is not recommended as it is seldom possible to achieve adequate deflection and the marking may not be sufficiently conspicuous at higher speeds.

8.12 Two size ranges are prescribed for the mini-roundabout marking (see figure 8-2); the choice will depend on the road space available and the need for conspicuity. The larger range should be used wherever it is needed to provide adequate deflection and deter straight through movement. The smaller range may be adequate at more constricted sites where the marking would otherwise occupy too large a part of the carriageway space and might be confusing, or where frequent overrunning would result in excessive maintenance costs.

8.13 In no circumstances may annular rings be added around the central disc. If a more conspicuous central marking is necessary, a larger disc, up to a maximum of 4 m should be used. If the junction area is very large, the diameter of the circulatory arrow marking should be increased to a maximum of 10 m, with the length of the arrows correspondingly increased to 4.45 m. Conspicuity may be further enhanced by replacing the normal central warning line on the approach with a hatched marking to diagram 1040.

8.14 The central disc of the mini-roundabout marking may be domed up to a maximum height of 125 mm (regulation 32(2)(c)), but must not exceed 6 mm at the perimeter. This will increase the conspicuity of the roundabout, particularly in wet weather. However, research evidence indicates that accident rates at domed roundabouts are slightly higher than at flush roundabouts, although the accident severity is less. The dome may be formed in bituminous or other suitable material, but the surface must be coloured white and be retroreflective.

8.15 The standard Give Way marking used at mini-roundabouts is diagram 1003.3. When used at mini-roundabouts, it must be accompanied by the upright sign to diagram 611.1 and may be accompanied by diagram 1023. In certain circumstances the Give Way marking to diagram 1003 may be used (see para 8.17 and figure 8-3). Diagram 611.1 will normally be sited about 1.5 m in advance of the Give Way marking. This might have to be increased if the sign would not otherwise be clearly visible.

8.16 Road markings or small traffic islands should be placed so as to ensure some vehicle deflection on the approaches; hatched markings to diagram 1040 can often help. Physical islands should be kept free of all furniture except the "keep left" bollards and other essential signs. Where an existing junction is being converted to a mini-roundabout, it may not be practicable to achieve the ideal amount of deflection. However, this may be acceptable if approach speeds are low.

8.17 Where suitable deflection cannot be achieved, traffic entering the roundabout might, because of its approach speed, disregard the standard advisory Give Way line (diagram 1003.3). In such cases, the mandatory GIVE WAY sign to diagram 602 may be mounted on the same post and above the sign to diagram 611.1. The GIVE WAY sign should not be used where it could confuse drivers into giving way to traffic from the left as well as from the right, e.g. on the stem of a T-junction or on any arm of a four-way junction. When diagram 602 is used, it must be accompanied by diagram 1023 and by the Give Way marking to diagram 1003 (see figure 8-3).

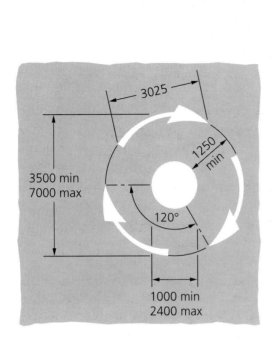

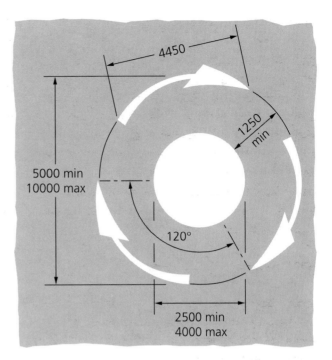

Diagram 1003.4 (alternative sizes)

Figure 8-2

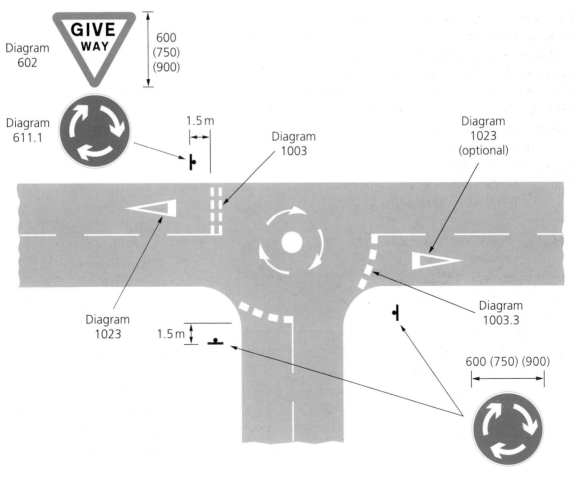

Figure 8-3

DOUBLE ROUNDABOUTS

8.18 These junctions have two conventional or mini-roundabouts either contiguous or connected by a central link road or kerbed island (see figure 8-4). Conventional and mini-roundabouts should not be mixed at the same junction.

8.19 Double roundabouts may offer an effective means of dealing with turning movements at asymmetrical junctions, those with a stagger, or junctions with high opposing right turn flows.

SIGNALLED ROUNDABOUTS

8.20 These have traffic signals in use on one or more of the approach arms for part or all of the day.

8.21 Where signals are used, traffic signal stop lines should be laid on the main circulating carriageway, approximately at right angles to the carriageway edge. The approach road should be marked as follows:

    (i)   full time signals - Stop line to diagram 1001, or

    (ii) part time signals - Stop line to diagram 1001 and Give Way line to diagram 1003.1. If the entry angle is such that the Stop and Give Way lines are coincident, or nearly so, the former may be omitted, but only with the written approval of the Secretary of State (see para 2.1).

LANE MARKINGS IN THE CIRCULATING AREA

8.22 Road markings may be used to channelise traffic and indicate which lane to use at and through roundabouts. Further details may be found in Advice Note TA 78/97 in the Design Manual for Roads and Bridges, Volume 6, (see para 1.4).

8.23 Lane markings can increase capacity by improving both the use of road space on the roundabout and the level of gap acceptance of

drivers joining it. They can also reduce the following types of accidents on roundabouts:

    (i)   side-to-side collisions on the circulating carriageway,

    (ii) drivers being forced onto the central island, and

    (iii) collisions between entering and circulating vehicles.

8.24 Markings should be designed to create flowing paths around the junction for all movements, avoiding sharp turns and providing a smooth alignment between entry and exit markings. Lane markings are always provided when the roundabout is under signal control. The route through the junction should be designed to avoid lane changing on the immediate approach to a stop line.

8.25 There are four basic configurations of road markings which may be used on the circulatory carriageway, making use of diagrams 1004/1004.1 and 1040.4. These are summarised below:

    (i)   concentric markings (see para 8.26),

    (ii) partial concentric markings (see para 8.27),

    (iii) concentric-spiral markings (see para 8.28), and

    (iv) spiral markings (see paras 8.29).

8.26 Concentric markings trace a complete path around the circulatory carriageway encouraging drivers to enter and circulate in two or more adjacent lanes.

8.27 Partial concentric markings differ from concentric markings in that their continuity around the circulatory carriageway is interrupted. They can assist on wide circulatory carriageways by presenting drivers with clearly defined lanes within which to pass around the junction, and reduce the likelihood of drivers in the off side entry lane being forced towards the central island.

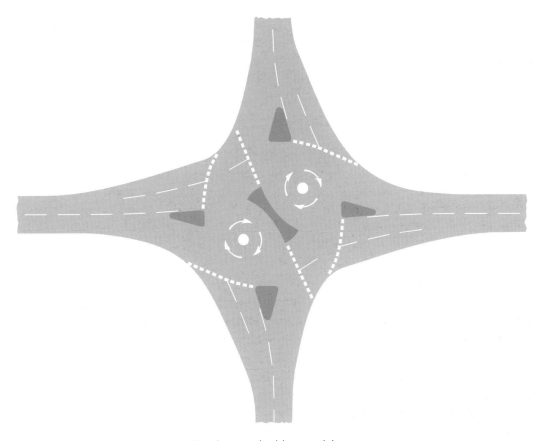

Contiguous double roundabout

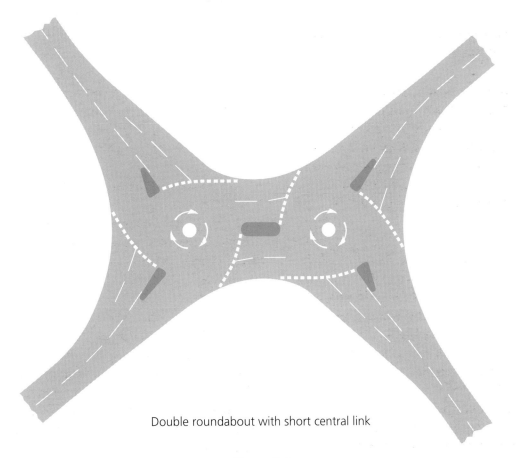

Double roundabout with short central link

Figure 8-4

8.28 Concentric-spiral markings are similar to concentric markings except that the outermost circulating lane or lanes guide traffic to the next exit by means of a lane drop. This is effected by running the circulatory markings directly into the existing road markings on that exit. They help to reduce conflicts between vehicles at the exits where more than one exit lane is provided, and can be used with any number of circulating lanes.

8.29 Spiral markings are more appropriate on larger roundabouts and involve a series of lane-gains and lane-drops around the circulatory carriageway so that drivers enter in the lane appropriate for their desired exit and follow that lane around the roundabout to be led off at the exit.

LANE DESTINATION MARKINGS AND ARROWS

8.30 Lane destination markings and arrows to diagrams 1035 and 1038 (see paras 13.1 to 13.5), may be justified where turning flows are consistently heavy throughout the day. Careful judgement is needed to ensure that such markings are not used inappropriately, as the reduction in flexibility may adversely affect the capacity of the roundabout.

8.31 Right turn arrows are best avoided on the approach lanes to a roundabout, other than a mini-roundabout, particularly as they can mislead overseas drivers used to driving on the right. Where a right hand lane is dedicated to a specific destination, this should be associated with an ahead arrow until the vehicle is in the circulatory carriageway.

8.32 Lane destinations and arrows may be used on the approach to and in the circulating areas of multiple lane signalled roundabouts, and those with circulatory markings (see paras 8.22 to 8.29). This may increase the capacity of a roundabout or make it safer, but will be successful only if drivers are given proper advance warning either by road markings or upright signs. The latter of course must be consistent with the markings.

8.33 Lane arrows and destinations will usually be repeated on roundabout circulatory carriageways when they have been used on the entries. They help drivers to identify the correct lane as early as possible and are particularly important if the lane is dedicated to a specific exit. They should also be used on the main carriageway of gyratory systems, i.e. large roundabouts formed of a series of one-way roads. Left turn arrows should not be used on the circulatory area immediately in advance of a point where a slip road enters from the left. This can confuse some drivers into turning left prematurely and travelling the wrong way along a dual carriageway. An ahead arrow may be used at this point, followed by a left turn arrow beyond the entering road.

SEGREGATED LEFT TURN LANES

8.34 Segregated left turn lanes reduce conflict between vehicles turning left at the first exit and those already circulating (see figure 8-5). The segregation may be effected by road markings to diagram 1041.1 or 1042.1, or by a physical island, in conjunction with the marking to diagram 1041 or 1042. Left turners are channelled into the left hand lane using lane arrows and road markings, supplemented by advance direction signs to diagram 2118 or its primary route equivalent (see Chapter 7, paras 5.43 and 5.44). Left turning vehicles proceed without having to give way to others circulating on the roundabout. Segregation by road markings is more common but may be less effective because it is liable to abuse. Further guidance may be found in TD51/03 in Volume 6 of the Design Manual for Roads and Bridges (see para 1.4).

8.35 If the left-turners are predominantly light vehicles and there is a high proportion of cyclists or heavy goods vehicles leaving the roundabout, differential speeds in adjacent lanes could cause problems, particularly if there is an uphill gradient. This might be especially hazardous for cyclists.

8.36 The use of these lanes in urban areas where pedestrians might cross should be considered carefully. Pedestrians should never be expected to cross left turn lanes segregated only by road markings. If pedestrians are likely to be present, they should be guided to a safer crossing point using guard rail or suitable planting. If this is not possible, segregation should be effected by a physical island of sufficient width to accommodate the peak number of pedestrians.

8.37 Segregated left turn lanes may encourage higher speeds; any desirable speed reduction measures should be applied before entry to the lane and not within it. Where the proportion of large goods vehicles is high, it should be ensured that the lane width is sufficient to accommodate the swept paths of larger vehicles, especially where physical segregation is provided. Where few such vehicles are expected, the lane may be reduced to 3.5 m in width, or exceptionally to an absolute minimum of 3.3 m. Where road markings to diagram 1041.1 or 1042.1 are used to create the lane segregation, the overall width of the marking should normally be at least 1 m. Where reflecting road studs are used, these must be red (see para 6.9).

8.38 When segregation is achieved using road markings alone, no special allowance needs to be made for broken-down vehicles, as other traffic will not be prevented from passing. Where physical segregation is introduced, the design should not prevent vehicles from making a left turn at the roundabout in the normal way by using the non-segregated part of the approach.

YELLOW BOX MARKINGS

8.39 Direction 35 prohibits the use of yellow box markings (see section 12) at unsignalled intersections on roundabouts. This is because a circulating vehicle has priority over those entering. If it stops to avoid obstructing the box when its exit is blocked, thereby releasing the flow of entering vehicles, there is likely to be uncertainty over re-establishing right of way when the exit is clear again. Moreover, a vehicle stopped in an outer lane might obscure vehicles lawfully continuing to circulate on the inner lanes (whose exit might not be blocked) from the view of drivers entering the roundabout. Yellow box markings may however be used where traffic entering the roundabout is controlled by signals at all times.

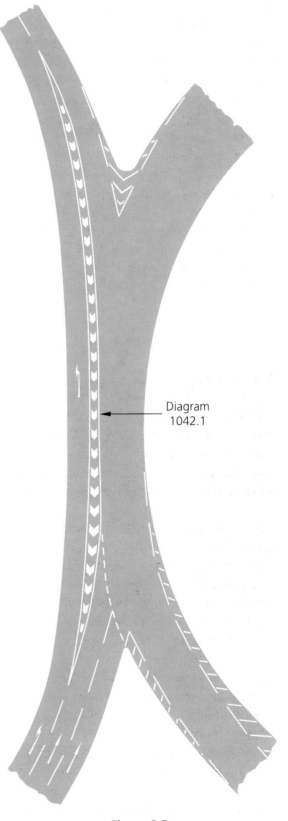

Diagram 1042.1

Figure 8-5

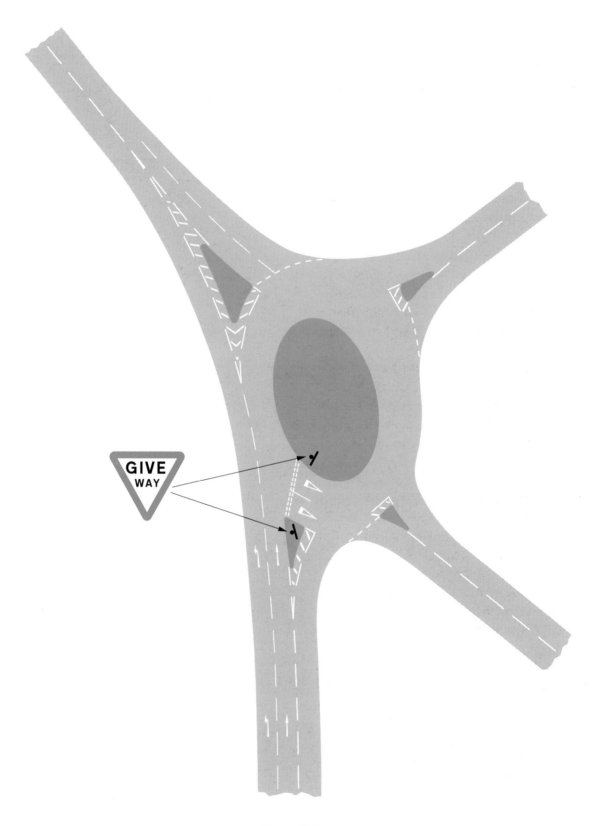

Figure 8-6

8.40 Although the Directions do not prohibit the use of the KEEP CLEAR marking (diagram 1026) on roundabouts, there are still the potential problems of obscuration of sight lines and re-establishing priorities. These risks should be assessed carefully when considering whether the marking might help resolve exit blocking problems.

YELLOW BAR MARKINGS

8.41 For details of the use of yellow bar markings on the approach to a roundabout see section 11.

SPECIAL CASES

8.42 It is sometimes expedient to give traffic from one arm of a roundabout priority over traffic already circulating. This might be necessary if the layout is unusual or there is a heavily dominant flow, but is likely to be more appropriate on urban roads, where speeds are lower, than in rural areas. As such a layout operates contrary to the conventional Give Way rule, it can be confusing and potentially dangerous. Traffic signal control may be a better option.

8.43 Where signalling the roundabout is not practicable, the layout in figure 8-6 may be used. The mandatory Give Way lines and triangle marking (diagrams 1003 and 1023) must be laid across the circulating area of the roundabout at the point of entry of the priority road. The Give Way markings should be reinforced by the provision of two upright GIVE WAY signs to diagram 602 as shown.

8.44 Give Way markings to diagram 1003 may also be used at conventional roundabouts (although only in conjunction with upright signs to diagram 602, see direction 34(1)), where there might otherwise be uncertainty about priorities, e.g. where drivers might be confused by a green signal at a pedestrian crossing immediately before the roundabout.

9 SIGNAL CONTROLLED JUNCTIONS

GENERAL

9.1 Effective marking of the approaches to signal controlled junctions is essential if the signals are to operate at their maximum efficiency. To achieve this:

   (i)   the Stop line (diagram 1001) should be sited as near as practicable to the intersection, consistent with driver and pedestrian needs. Drivers waiting at the Stop line must have an uninterrupted view of at least one signal,

   (ii)   lane lines should be arranged to secure the maximum use of available carriageway space consistent with adequate lane width, and

   (iii)   where lanes are dedicated to a particular turning movement, the appropriate lane destination arrows should be provided at the commencement of the lane, and repeated as necessary (see also paras 9.9 and 13.1 to 13.3).

9.2 Figure 9-1 shows the standard layout of the Stop lines, signals and pedestrian crossings at a signal controlled junction having a different number of lanes on each approach. It also shows a left turn lane governed by priority markings instead of being under direct signal control.

9.3 Figure 9-2 shows a typical arrangement of lane and centre of carriageway markings at a signal controlled junction where a six-lane road subject to a 40 mph speed limit meets a four-lane road subject to a 30 mph speed limit.

STOP LINES

9.4 These are described in section 3. The Stop line should be positioned a minimum of 1.5 m in advance of the near side primary signal, although 2.5 m should be used where practicable. The marking should be positioned at right angles to the centre line of the carriageway, even at skew junctions.

9.5 At difficult sites, Stop lines and near side primary signals need to be located sufficiently far back from the junction to enable long vehicles to turn into that road without being blocked by vehicles waiting at the Stop line. This will however reduce junction capacity and it may be necessary to consider prohibiting the turn.

9.6 Guidance on the use of advanced stop lines for cyclists will be found in paras 16.20 to 16.22.

LONGITUDINAL MARKINGS

9.7 On the immediate approach to the signals, the normal lane marking (diagram 1005 or 1005.1) and the centre of carriageway marking (diagram 1008 or 1008.1) should change to the warning line versions (diagram 1004 or 1004.1). Table 4-3 gives details of the size and minimum number of marks recommended.

9.8 Lane markings may be laid within the junction where some guidance to traffic would be helpful, although care should be taken that the meaning is clear to drivers on all approaches and there is no risk of giving the impression of a Stop or Give Way line to transverse movements. The arrow to diagram 1038.1 (see figure 13-4) may be used to indicate a route through a junction, or used in pairs to indicate that opposing right-turning traffic should pass near side to near side (see figure 13-5). Further details can be found in paras 13.7 and 13.8.

LANE DESTINATION MARKINGS

9.9 It is essential that drivers are made aware in good time of the correct lane to use at signalled junctions. Where lanes are indicated for left or right turn movements only, it is particularly important that early notice is given by the use of the appropriate lane arrow, repeated as necessary. If this is neglected, drivers are likely to become trapped in the wrong lane. A lane arrow should be used at the start of a newly formed lane, and at heavily-trafficked junctions the lane markings should be extended sufficiently far upstream to cope with peak flows. The use of lane

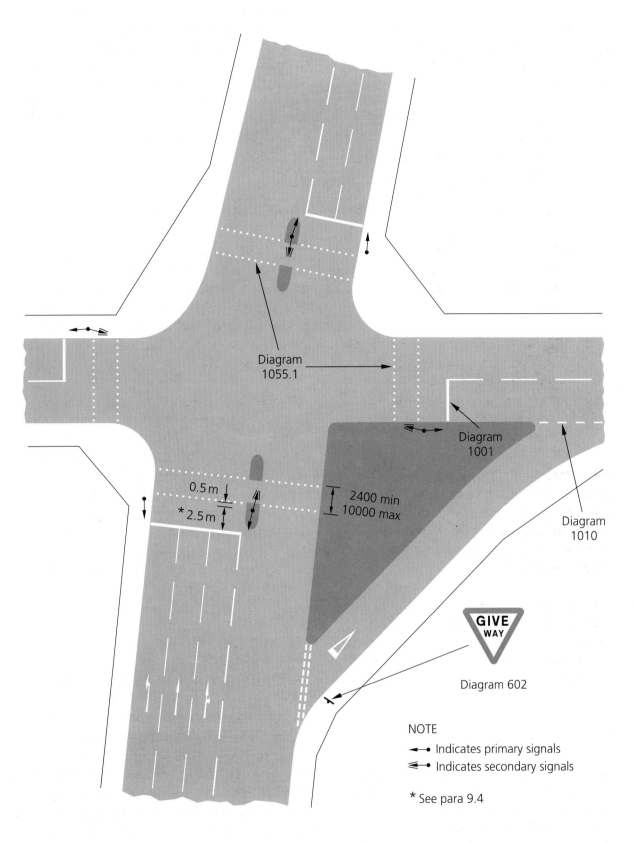

Diagram
1055.1

Diagram
1001

Diagram
1010

0.5 m

* 2.5 m

2400 min
10000 max

GIVE
WAY

Diagram 602

NOTE
●——● Indicates primary signals
≼——● Indicates secondary signals

* See para 9.4

Figure 9-1

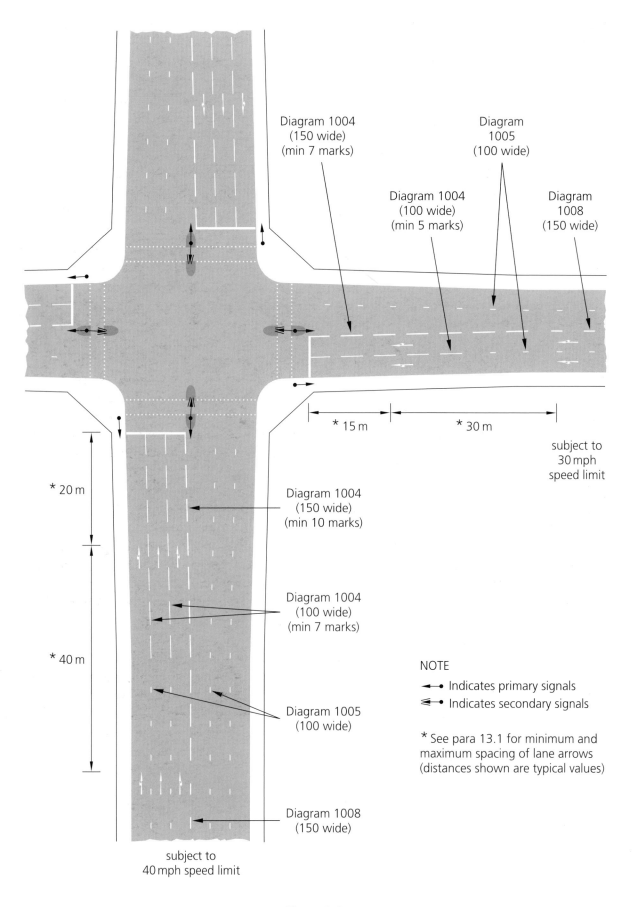

Diagram 1004
(150 wide)
(min 7 marks)

Diagram
1005
(100 wide)

Diagram 1004
(100 wide)
(min 5 marks)

Diagram
1008
(150 wide)

* 15 m   * 30 m

subject to
30 mph
speed limit

Diagram 1004
(150 wide)
(min 10 marks)

* 20 m

Diagram 1004
(100 wide)
(min 7 marks)

* 40 m

Diagram 1005
(100 wide)

NOTE

⊶ Indicates primary signals

⇜• Indicates secondary signals

* See para 13.1 for minimum and
maximum spacing of lane arrows
(distances shown are typical values)

Diagram 1008
(150 wide)

subject to
40 mph speed limit

Figure 9-2

arrows and lane destination markings is described in paras 13.1 to 13.5, and para 13.6 indicates where traffic regulation orders are required.

LANE WIDTHS

9.10 With new junctions, entry lane widths should be between 3 and 3.65 m, unless there are specific reasons to justify the use of narrower or wider lane widths. Where an existing junction is being improved or modified and available road space is restricted, then the permitted lane widths for straight ahead entry lanes may be reduced to 2.5 m provided that the 85th percentile approach speed does not exceed 56 kph (35 mph) and the reduced width enables a necessary extra lane to be provided. In exceptional circumstances, lane widths may be reduced to 2.25 m where it is not intended to make provision for large goods vehicles.

9.11 In all cases the lane and centre line markings (both varied to the warning module) should meet the Stop line.

9.12 The number of lanes on the exit side of the junction should match the number of ahead lanes at the Stop line. If localised widening of an exit is necessary to achieve this, the subsequent reduction in the number of lanes should be carried out beyond the junction over a distance of at least 100 m for a single lane reduction. Deflection arrows to diagram 1014 may be used to warn of the impending loss. Normally, it should be the right hand lane that is lost, so that slower vehicles are not required to merge with faster-moving accelerating traffic. In order to maintain capacity at signalled junctions, it is important to keep the exits as well as the approaches clear of parked vehicles.

PEDESTRIAN CROSSING POINTS

9.13 If a pedestrian crossing point is provided at a signalled junction, whether itself signalled or not, the Stop line should be placed a minimum of 1.5 m in advance of the left hand side primary signal post, which should be 0.5 m from the nearer row of studs (diagram 1055.1). See also paras 6.15 and 9.4. Although previous advice was to position the signal head 1 m in advance of the crossing studs, this is excessive where tactile paving is used. The tactile surface is intended to lead people to the push button box; a gap of 1 m between the edge of the tactile surface and the box is too great to ensure this.

9.14 The width of the crossing is dependent upon site conditions, but is normally in the range 2.4 to 5 m. Exceptional numbers of pedestrians may require the width to be increased to a maximum of 10 m. Dropped kerbs and tactile paving should be provided at all crossing points. Where pedestrian refuges are provided, the full width of the crossing should be maintained through the refuge as a dropped kerb or flush with the carriageway.

UNSIGNALLED VEHICLE MOVEMENTS

9.15 Where a left turn slip road is provided outside the control of the traffic signals, Give Way markings to diagram 1003, the warning triangle to diagram 1023 and the upright sign to diagram 602 should be used (see figure 9-1). If visibility is such that a Stop line would be justified, the left turn should be brought under signal control. A left turn slip lane should be separated from the other lanes by a traffic island. If no provision is made for pedestrians, they are likely to have difficulty in crossing an unsignalled slip road in an otherwise signalled junction.

10 GRADE SEPARATED JUNCTIONS

DESIGN

10.1 Grade separated junctions may involve merging and diverging lanes, or the gain or loss of lanes, or a combination of these. As junctions become more complex, so road marking layouts become more complicated. It is not practicable to detail all possibilities, but the standard principles should be followed. Reference should be made to TD 22/92 in Volume 6 of the Design Manual for Roads and Bridges (see para 1.4) for further guidance. When designing a complex layout, it should be borne in mind that it must be capable of being signed and marked in a way that drivers can readily understand.

MERGING AND DIVERGING SLIP ROADS

10.2 The layout of markings and road studs at the simplest grade separated junction is shown in figure 10-1. The principal dimensions are detailed in tables 10-1 and 10-2. This arrangement is suitable for one or two-lane exit and one-lane entry slip roads.

10.3 The nosing of the slip road is marked using diagram 1042 (varied where appropriate to reverse the direction of the chevrons, see para 4.62). Red studs are provided at 3 m centres along the outside of both edges.

Table 10-1 Merge and lane-gain markings

Road type	Speed limit (mph)	Length of entry taper (m) (1)	Taper for minimum angle at nose (2)	Nose length (m) (3)	Length of ghost island tail (m) (4)	Width of diag 1010 marking (mm)
Rural motorway	70	205	1 in 40	115	180	200
Rural dual carriageway	70	150	1 in 30	85	150	200
	60 or less	130	1 in 25	75	150	150
Urban road	60	95	1 in 15	50	n/a	150
	50 or less	75	1 in 12	40	n/a	150

NOTE: Numbers (1) to (4) at the head of the above columns relate to features shown on figures 10-1 to 10-6.

Table 10-2 Diverge and lane-drop markings

Road type	Speed limit (mph)	Length of exit taper (m)		Taper for minimum angle at nose (7)[2]	Nose length (m) (8)[2]	Width of diag 1010 marking (mm)
		1 lane (5)[2]	2 lanes (6)[1,2]			
Rural motorway	70	170	185 (150)	1 in 15	80	200
Rural dual carriageway	70	150	150 (120)	1 in 15	70	200
	60	130	130 (110)	1 in 15	70	150
Urban road	60	95	110 (90)	1 in 15	50	150
	50 or less	75	90 (75)	1 in 12	40	150

NOTES
1. Taper lengths refer to 2 x 3.65 m lanes, or, in brackets, 2 x 3.00m lanes.
2. Numbers (5) to (8) at the head of the above columns relate to features shown on figures 10-1 and 10-7.

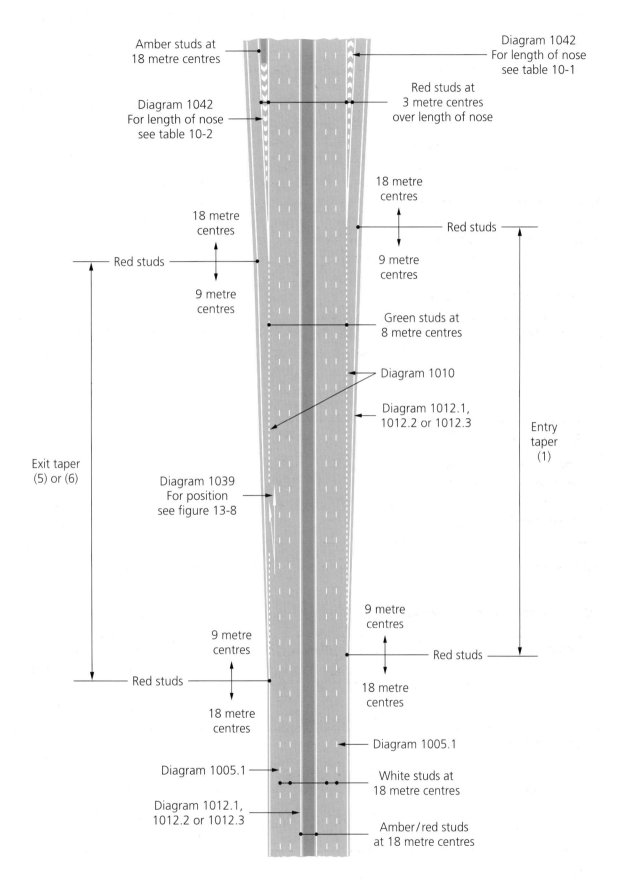

Amber studs at 18 metre centres

Diagram 1042 For length of nose see table 10-1

Diagram 1042 For length of nose see table 10-2

Red studs at 3 metre centres over length of nose

18 metre centres

Red studs

9 metre centres

18 metre centres

Red studs

9 metre centres

Green studs at 8 metre centres

Diagram 1010

Diagram 1012.1, 1012.2 or 1012.3

Entry taper (1)

Exit taper (5) or (6)

Diagram 1039 For position see figure 13-8

9 metre centres

Red studs

9 metre centres

Red studs

18 metre centres

18 metre centres

Diagram 1005.1

Diagram 1005.1

White studs at 18 metre centres

Diagram 1012.1, 1012.2 or 1012.3

Amber/red studs at 18 metre centres

Figure 10-1

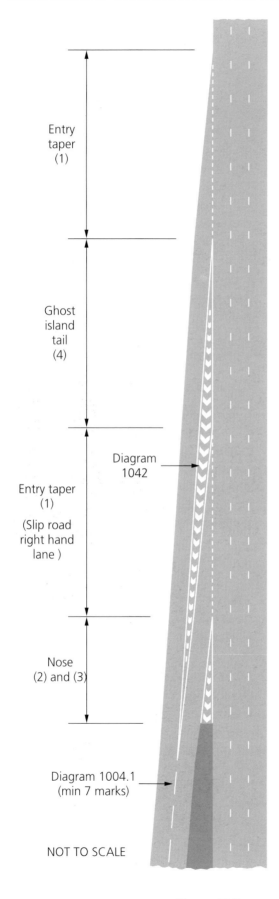

Entry
taper
(1)

Ghost
island
tail
(4)

Diagram
1042

Entry taper
(1)

(Slip road
right hand
lane)

Nose
(2) and (3)

Diagram 1004.1
(min 7 marks)

NOT TO SCALE

Figure 10-2

10.4 The edge line should be continued along the slip road. Where raised rib markings are used, the rib spacing should be reduced to 250 mm on motorway slip roads. Red reflecting road studs should be used on the near side and amber on the off side, both at 18 m centres except as detailed in para 10.5.

10.5 The main carriageway edge line should change to diagram 1010, with green reflecting road studs at 8 m centres, across the slip road over which traffic joins or leaves. Along the same length, the spacing of the red studs associated with the edge line to diagram 1012.1, 1012.2 or 1012.3 at the near side of the slip road is reduced from 18 m to 9 m. The bifurcation arrow to diagram 1039 should be used as shown in figure 13-8 at the lengths specified in para 13.12.

10.6 Conventional lane lines to diagram 1005 or 1005.1 (see table 10-4) on the main carriageway should be continued through the junction.

10.7 An entry layout for two-lane slip roads is shown in figure 10-2, allowing each lane of the slip road to join separately. The ghost island between the joining lanes should be to diagram 1042, bordered by red studs. This layout is suitable where the main line flow is light, the main carriageway is three or more lanes wide and the merging flow exceeds the capacity of a single lane.

LANE GAINS

10.8 The principal dimensions for lane-gain layouts are given in table 10-1. There are two basic situations; the number of lanes gained will either be the same as, or less than, the number of lanes on the entry slip road.

10.9 Where the number of lanes gained equals the number of lanes on the entry slip road, the markings in figure 10-3 should be used. All lane markings to diagram 1005.1 on both the main carriageway and the slip road should change to 1004.1 as indicated (or from 1005 to 1004 on roads where the speed limit is not more than 40 mph; see table 10-4). If only one lane is gained, the ghost island is not used.

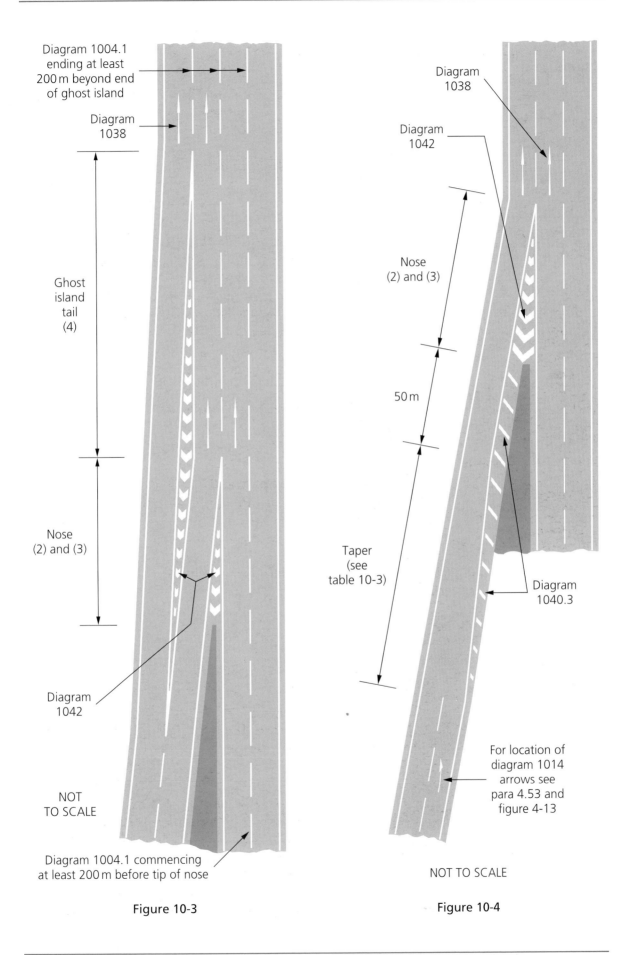

Diagram 1004.1 ending at least 200 m beyond end of ghost island

Diagram 1038

Ghost island tail (4)

Nose (2) and (3)

Diagram 1042

NOT TO SCALE

Diagram 1004.1 commencing at least 200 m before tip of nose

Figure 10-3

Diagram 1038

Diagram 1042

Nose (2) and (3)

50 m

Taper (see table 10-3)

Diagram 1040.3

For location of diagram 1014 arrows see para 4.53 and figure 4-13

NOT TO SCALE

Figure 10-4

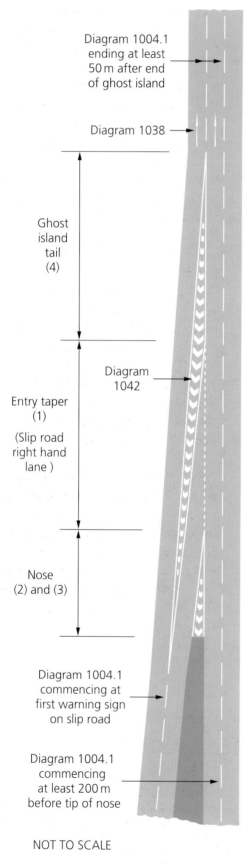

Diagram 1004.1 ending at least 50 m after end of ghost island

Diagram 1038

Ghost island tail (4)

Diagram 1042

Entry taper (1)

(Slip road right hand lane)

Nose (2) and (3)

Diagram 1004.1 commencing at first warning sign on slip road

Diagram 1004.1 commencing at least 200 m before tip of nose

NOT TO SCALE

Figure 10-5

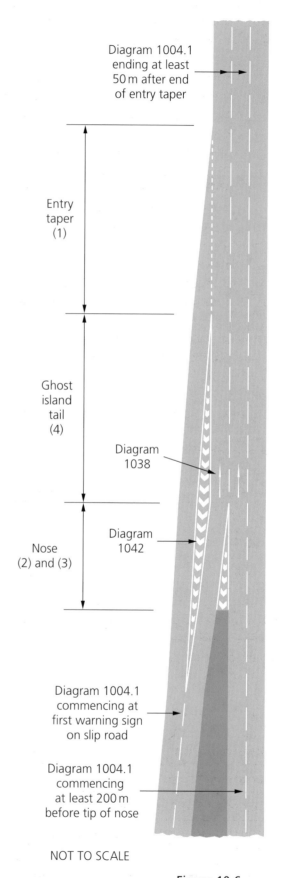

Diagram 1004.1 ending at least 50 m after end of entry taper

Entry taper (1)

Ghost island tail (4)

Diagram 1038

Diagram 1042

Nose (2) and (3)

Diagram 1004.1 commencing at first warning sign on slip road

Diagram 1004.1 commencing at least 200 m before tip of nose

NOT TO SCALE

Figure 10-6

10.10 Where the number of lanes gained is less than the number of lanes on the entry slip road, there are three methods of carrying out the merge:

(i) the two-lane slip road is reduced to one lane in advance of the back of the nose, so that the number of lanes on the entry slip road equals the number of lanes gained. The lane reduction should be effected by the use of hatched markings to diagram 1040.3 (see para 4.53 and figure 10-4). The taper length should be determined from table 10-3 and the full reduction in width achieved 50 m in advance of the back of the nose. The hatching should then be extended to the end of the slip road to form part of the nose. Additionally, at least two deflection arrows to diagram 1014 should be placed in the lane which is to be discontinued. The tip of the final arrow

should be 30 m before the start of the taper and preceding arrows at intervals of 30 m in advance of that. The markings should be supplemented by signs to diagram 872.1,

(ii) the right hand slip lane merges with the through carriageway before the left hand slip lane is added (figure 10-5). All lane markings to diagrams 1005 or 1005.1 should change to 1004 or 1004.1 respectively (see table 10-4), commencing at the first sign to diagram 874 on the slip road and at least 200 m prior to the merge nose tip on the main carriageway. These markings should be continued for at least 50 m beyond the termination of the ghost island. Road markings to diagram 1010 should extend from the tip of the merge nose to the point where it meets the ghost island. Ahead arrows to diagram 1038 should be placed on the joining (additional) lane and on the original left lane of the main carriageway at the point they come together, to discourage premature lane changing,

(iii) the left hand slip lane merges with the additional main carriageway lane after the right hand slip lane has been added to the through carriageway (figure 10-6). In this option it is not easy for slower slip road traffic to merge into the faster lanes; it is also difficult to sign. Reference should be made to the appropriate overseeing authority before it is used.

Table 10-3 Taper for slip road lane reduction

85 percentile speed (mph)	Preferred minimum taper	Absolute minimum taper
30	1 in 40	1 in 20
40	1 in 40	1 in 30
50	1 in 45	1 in 40
60	1 in 50	1 in 50
70	1 in 55	1 in 55

NOTE: The preferred minimum taper should be used wherever practicable; the absolute minimum should be used only where unavoidable.

Table 10-4 Size of markings in figures 10-1 to 10-7

Diagram number		Size of marking (Length x Gap x Width)			
Speed limit (mph)		Speed limit (mph)			
40 or less	50 to 70	40 or less	50	60	70
1004	1004.1	4 m x 2 m x 100 mm	6 m x 3 m x 150 mm	6 m x 3 m x 150 mm	6 m x 3 m x 150 mm
1005	1005.1	1 m x 5 m x 100 mm	2 m x 7 m x 150 mm	2 m x 7 m x 150 mm	2 m x 7 m x 150 mm
1010	1010	1 m x 1 m x 100 mm	1 m x 1 m x 150 mm	1 m x 1 m x 150 mm	1 m x 1 m x 200 mm

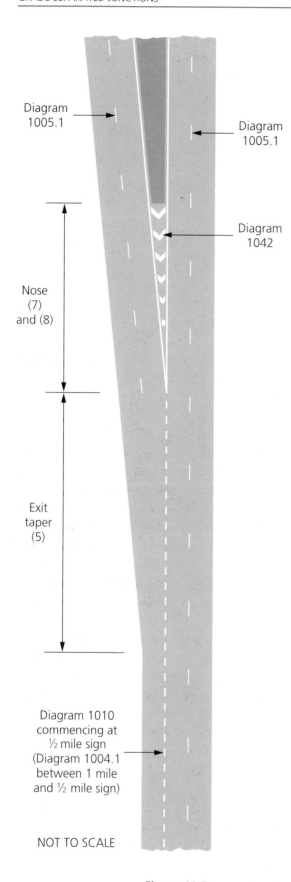

Diagram 1005.1

Diagram 1005.1

Diagram 1042

Nose (7) and (8)

Exit taper (5)

Diagram 1010 commencing at ½ mile sign (Diagram 1004.1 between 1 mile and ½ mile sign)

NOT TO SCALE

Figure 10-7

LANE DROPS

10.11 A standard lane-drop layout for high speed roads is shown in figure 10-7. The lane markings dividing the through lanes from the lane or lanes to be dropped should change to diagram 1004.1 (see table 10-4 for width) at the one mile advance direction sign. From the half-mile advance direction sign to the diverge nose tip, the marking changes again to diagram 1010. Road studs used in conjunction with the diagram 1010 marking must be green. The studs will be spaced 18 metres apart from the half-mile sign to the final advance direction sign, then closed up to 8 metre centres to the tip of the diverge nose. On lower-speed roads, or where the advance direction signs are sited at two thirds and one third of a mile from the junction, the lane-drop markings will commence later and the stud spacings adjusted to suit. The appropriate widths and modules for these markings are detailed in table 10-4.

10.12 The principal dimensions for lane-drop layouts are given in table 10-2. The table indicates the length of the exit taper depending upon the number of extra lanes provided on the slip road. In the case of the lane drop shown in figure 10-7, two lanes on the slip road represents an increase of one over the approach lane and therefore the taper length shown in the table should be as indicated under the heading (5).

AUXILIARY LANES

10.13 Auxiliary lanes are additional lanes at the side of the main carriageway between the nose and the entry or exit taper at a junction. They are used at merge and diverge junctions and also at lane gain and lane drop junctions, and increase capacity by providing increased merge or diverge opportunity and additional space for weaving. They are separated from the main carriageway by the marking to diagram 1010. Further details may be found in TD 22/92 in Volume 6 of the Design Manual for Roads and Bridges (see para 1.4).

11 YELLOW BAR MARKINGS

11.1 Yellow bar markings are used in certain conditions on high speed approaches to roundabouts, either on the main carriageway or on an exit slip road. They have been shown to be effective in reducing accidents associated with speed adaptation, i.e. where drivers have been travelling at sustained high speed for long periods. The types of accidents most likely to be influenced are single vehicle and overrun accidents. The markings should not be used in an attempt to reduce speeds at sharp bends or other hazards. They are not normally appropriate on slip roads if there is a segregated left turn lane for the roundabout, or at roundabouts controlled by traffic signals. On approaching a green signal, some drivers will slow down in response to the markings, others will maintain speed in an attempt to beat a change to red. Markings are unlikely to be approved in such cases unless the accident justification is strong.

11.2 Before use of the markings is contemplated, it is essential to ensure that all standard signing has been correctly installed. The warning signs described in Chapter 4 (paras 2.13 to 2.18) should be provided and be of the appropriate sizes. All signs should be checked to ensure they are in good condition and not obscured e.g. by vegetation, and sited at the correct distances from the junction. Only then should treatment with yellow bar markings be considered.

11.3 The markings are not prescribed in the Traffic Signs Regulations and General Directions 2002. However, for installations in Northern Ireland, where they are prescribed for use at roundabouts on dual carriageway roads only, reference should be made to Appendix A. Elsewhere, written authorisation from the Secretary of State will need to be obtained for each site where it is proposed to use them (see para 2.1). Authorisation will normally be given only where the following criteria are met:

(i) the carriageway on which they are to be laid is a one-way approach to a roundabout (i.e. a dual carriageway or an exit slip road),

(ii) there is at least 3 km of dual carriageway in advance of the site, with no major intersections or bends with a horizontal radius less than the desirable minimum for a 120 kph design speed shown in table 3 of TD 9/93 in Volume 6 of the Design Manual for Roads and Bridges (see para 1.4),

(iii) the road is subject to the national speed limit of 70 mph, and

(iv) the accident record for the roundabout includes at least three accidents involving personal injury during the preceding three years, in which speed on the relevant approach was a contributory factor.

11.4 Each approach to a given roundabout is treated as a separate site and the use of the markings on each approach must be justified independently. The application of the criteria in para 11.3 will ensure that the markings are used only at sites where they are likely to make a positive contribution to safety.

11.5 The marking consists of 90 yellow transverse bars on main carriageways, and 45 on slip roads. The bars are 600 mm wide, and are laid at right angles to the centre line of the carriageway (see figure 11-1 for details of the layout on a main carriageway). The first bar is laid at a distance of 50 m measured along the centre line of the carriageway in advance of the Give Way line. Successive bars are spaced in accordance with the running measurements in table 11-1 for main carriageways and in table 11-2 for slip roads.

11.6 To assist surface water drainage, each end of each bar should be terminated about 150 mm from the edge of the carriageway or the edge line marking if provided. This may be increased to 750 mm where there is a particular drainage problem, or if there are significant numbers of cyclists. Bars should not be extended across hard strips or hard shoulders as this would give the impression that these are traffic lanes.

11.7 Skid resistance of the bars should not be less than 55. Drop-on glass beads should not be applied. The bars should not exceed 5 mm in thickness, and the combined thickness of the bars and any superimposed marking must not exceed 6 mm. Although thinner markings might need more frequent renewal, they are less likely to result in noise levels which are unacceptable to local residents.

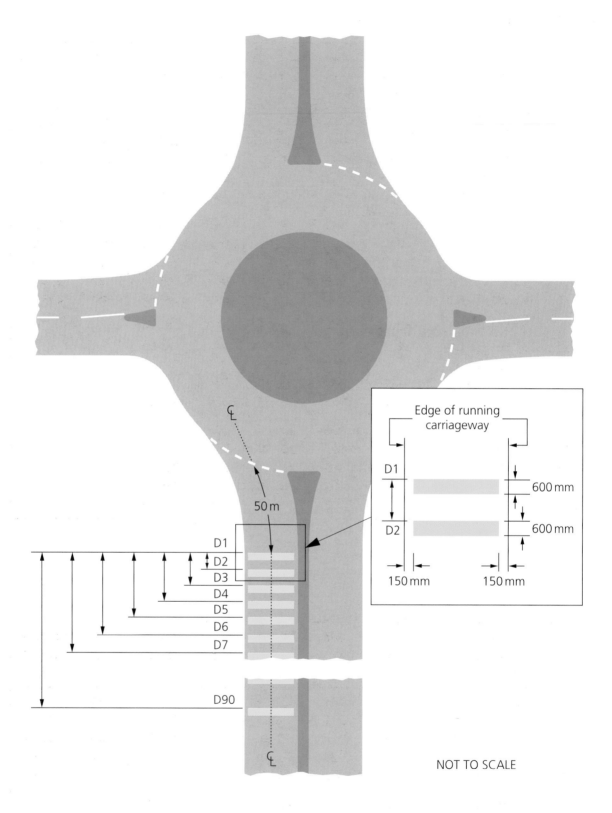

NOT TO SCALE

NOTE: The 150 mm gap between the edge of the running carriageway and the bar edges can be increased on the left hand side to a maximum of 750 mm at sites where there are particular problems with surface water drainage or where there is a significant number of cyclists.

Figure 11-1

Table 11-1 Spacing of bars on main carriageway

Bar No.	Distance from D1 (m)	Bar No.	Distance from D1 (m)	Bar No.	Distance from D1 (m)	Bar No.	Distance from D1 (m)	Bar No.	Distance from D1 (m)
D1	0.00	D21	60.10	D41	133.75	D61	224.70	D81	338.15
D2	2.75	D22	63.45	D42	137.85	D62	229.80	D82	344.65
D3	5.50	D23	66.80	D43	142.00	D63	234.90	D83	351.35
D4	8.25	D24	70.15	D44	146.15	D64	240.10	D84	358.30
D5	11.05	D25	73.60	D45	150.40	D65	245.40	D85	365.50
D6	13.90	D26	77.05	D46	154.65	D66	250.70	D86	373.20
D7	16.80	D27	80.55	D47	158.95	D67	256.10	D87	380.90
D8	19.70	D28	84.10	D48	163.35	D68	261.50	D88	388.60
D9	22.60	D29	87.65	D49	167.75	D69	267.00	D89	396.25
D10	25.55	D30	91.30	D50	172.25	D70	272.60	D90	403.95
D11	28.55	D31	94.95	D51	176.75	D71	278.20		
D12	31.60	D32	98.65	D52	181.30	D72	283.90		
D13	34.65	D33	102.40	D53	185.95	D73	289.60		
D14	37.70	D34	106.15	D54	190.60	D74	295.45		
D15	40.80	D35	110.00	D55	195.35	D75	301.30		
D16	43.95	D36	113.85	D56	200.10	D76	307.25		
D17	47.15	D37	117.75	D57	204.90	D77	313.30		
D18	50.35	D38	121.70	D58	209.80	D78	319.35		
D19	53.55	D39	125.65	D59	214.70	D79	325.55		
D20	56.80	D40	129.70	D60	219.70	D80	331.75		

Table 11-2 Spacing of bars on slip roads

Bar No.	Distance from D1 (m)	Bar No.	Distance from D1 (m)	Bar No.	Distance from D1 (m)	Bar No.	Distance from D1 (m)	Bar No.	Distance from D1 (m)
D1	0.00	D11	30.20	D21	67.20	D31	112.90	D41	170.00
D2	2.75	D12	33.55	D22	71.35	D32	118.00	D42	176.70
D3	5.55	D13	37.00	D23	75.60	D33	123.30	D43	183.90
D4	8.45	D14	40.50	D24	79.90	D34	128.70	D44	191.60
D5	11.35	D15	44.05	D25	84.30	D35	134.20	D45	199.30
D6	14.35	D16	47.70	D26	88.80	D36	139.80		
D7	17.40	D17	51.45	D27	93.45	D37	145.50		
D8	20.50	D18	55.30	D28	98.20	D38	151.35		
D9	23.70	D19	59.20	D29	103.00	D39	157.40		
D10	26.90	D20	63.15	D30	107.90	D40	163.60		

12 YELLOW BOX JUNCTION MARKINGS

12.1 Part II of Schedule 19 to the Regulations defines two purposes for the yellow box marking to diagram 1043 or 1044 (see figure 12-1):

(i) to mark an area of carriageway conveying the prohibition that no person shall cause a vehicle to enter the box junction so that it has to stop within it due to the presence of stationary vehicles. A vehicle waiting to turn right (other than at a roundabout) may stop within the box junction for so long as it is prevented from completing the right turn by oncoming vehicles or other vehicles which are stationary whilst waiting to complete a right turn.

(ii) when placed in conjunction with diagrams 615 and 811 on an area of carriageway which is less than 4.5 m wide at its narrowest point, the road marking shall convey the prohibition that no person shall cause a vehicle to enter the box junction so that the vehicle has to stop within it due to the presence of oncoming vehicles or other stationary vehicles beyond the box.

12.2 Drivers entering the box when their exit is obstructed by stationary vehicles, whether in the road ahead or to either side, commit an offence. It is permissible, however, to enter and become stationary if turning right and prevented from leaving the junction only by oncoming traffic, or by other vehicles waiting to complete the right turn.

12.3 The Directions do not permit the use of yellow box markings at roundabouts unless traffic entering the box is controlled by signals at all times (see para 8.39 and direction 35). Nor should they be used where traffic streams merge, as it will not be clear which stream has precedence when a gap appears.

12.4 Traffic regulation orders are not needed in order to install yellow box markings, although the police should always be consulted. The marking is subject to section 36 of the Road Traffic Act 1988 (see para 2.4 and regulation 10).

12.5 Experience has shown that the marking improves traffic flows where previously there were delays due to vehicles blocking the junction and impeding the cross flow. At signal controlled junctions, the queues of traffic left at the end of a green phase have been significantly reduced and there have been marked reductions in injury accidents, especially those involving pedestrians.

12.6 Box markings are no substitute for traffic signals. They can however help to improve traffic flow at junctions where blocking back causes obstruction. Their use at pinch points controlled by priority signs and at level crossings (diagram 1045) is dealt with in paras 12.13 and 12.14 respectively.

12.7 Not all junctions are suitable for the installation of box markings, and certain criteria should be applied before deciding whether a particular site should be marked. A traffic survey should be carried out to determine the extent of the problem, not only to assess the suitability of the junction for box marking but also to establish whether any alternative measures might be effective (e.g. re-timing or linking of traffic signals at adjacent junctions). A survey will also reveal what further measures might be needed, e.g. imposition of waiting and loading restrictions or re-location of bus stops.

12.8 Factors which influence a decision to provide box markings include the following:

(i) the junction should preferably, though not necessarily, be controlled by signals (see also para 12.3),

(ii) blocking back from a junction ahead should occur under existing conditions, even if only for short periods,

(iii) there should preferably be heavy traffic flows on both opposing arms of the junction. At unsignalled junctions with minor roads where blocking of the mouth of the minor road is infrequent, a KEEP CLEAR marking (see paras 22.11 to 22.14) may be more appropriate,

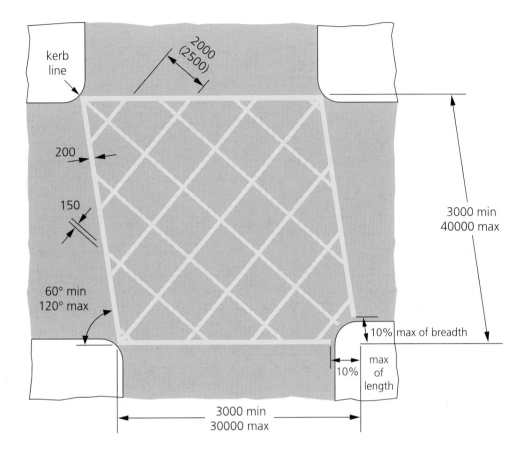

Diagram 1043

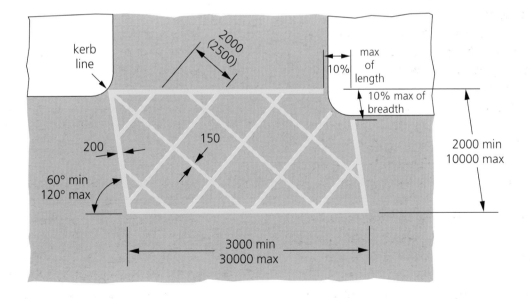

Diagram 1044

Figure 12-1

(iv) opposing roads at a junction should normally be in line with each other. The markings may, however, be used exceptionally at staggered junctions, particularly where the minor roads have a right hand stagger, provided the maximum box length is not exceeded, and irregular shapes can be avoided. Two half-boxes may be a practical substitute for a single large box in such circumstances,

(v) the carriageway beyond the junction should be free from obstruction (this may necessitate the imposition of waiting or loading restrictions, or the adjustment of bus stops on the lengths concerned),

(vi) where a succession of junctions gives rise to blocking back, the establishment of a series of boxes should be considered, provided at least 20 m storage space can be maintained between successive boxes, and

(vii) there should preferably not be a high proportion of right-turning traffic, since experience has shown that the effectiveness of the marking is reduced under these conditions.

12.9 Yellow box markings may be used outside police, fire, ambulance stations or hospitals only where there is an access road forming a junction with the main road. Where vehicles exit directly onto the carriageway, a KEEP CLEAR marking to diagram 1026 or a KEEP CLEAR marking to diagram 1027.1 (varied to omit the word "SCHOOL") should be used.

12.10 Half-boxes, in which only half the area of the junction is marked (diagram 1044) are appropriate at "T" junctions and other junctions where the traffic blocks back from one direction only. Half-boxes may be used only in the position shown in the lower drawing in figure 12-1, i.e. on the minor road side of the main carriageway.

SETTING OUT

12.11 The marking consists of yellow lines forming a box enclosing cross-hatched diagonal lines (see figure 12-1). The diagonal lines are 150 mm wide and spaced 2 m apart where the shortest boundary of the box is less than 9 m long, or 2.5 m apart where the shortest boundary line of the box is 9 m or more. Yellow box markings must always have four straight sides, each being approximately transverse to the traffic flow on the approach. Up to 10% of the length of the side at any corner may be cut away as shown in the diagram to accommodate corner kerbs. The overall shape of the marking and the number of cross-hatched lines will vary to accord with the circumstances at the site.

12.12 To set out the marking:

(i) mark transverse lines across each arm of the junction approximately at right angles to the flow of traffic (see figure 12-2),

(ii) where the corners of the box have been cut away, complete the full box with construction lines; where the sides are still unequal in length, extend the short sides to X and Q using construction lines so that PX = PY = YQ,

(iii) draw a main diagonal X-Y running from corner to corner of the notional box (either pair of opposite corners may be used),

(iv) construct a diagonal line P-Q' intersecting the first diagonal at right angles; it will not necessarily connect both corners of the yellow box,

(v) set out the intermediate lines parallel to the diagonals, at grid intervals of 2 m or 2.5 m as appropriate (see para 12.11).

Half-box markings should be designed in the same way as full box markings but with only half the box marked on the road (see lower drawing in figure 12-1).

SPECIAL CASES

12.13 Box markings are sometimes effective in combination with priority signs (diagrams 615/615.1 and 811/811.1) to break queues through an exceptionally narrow pinch point and enable an opposing flow to continue without unnecessary delay. The marking may be used for this purpose only if the carriageway width is less than 4.5 m at the narrowest point (regulation 29(2) and Part II of Schedule 19).

12.14 A different pattern of yellow box marking (diagram 1045) is used at Automatic Half Barrier level crossings (see paras 19.18 and 19.19). This may be appropriate at other forms of railway crossing if these are likely to become blocked by queuing traffic, but only with the agreement of the Railway Inspectorate. Further guidance on the use of box markings at level crossings can be found in paras 19.18 and 19.19, and at tramway crossings in paras 18.15 and 18.23.

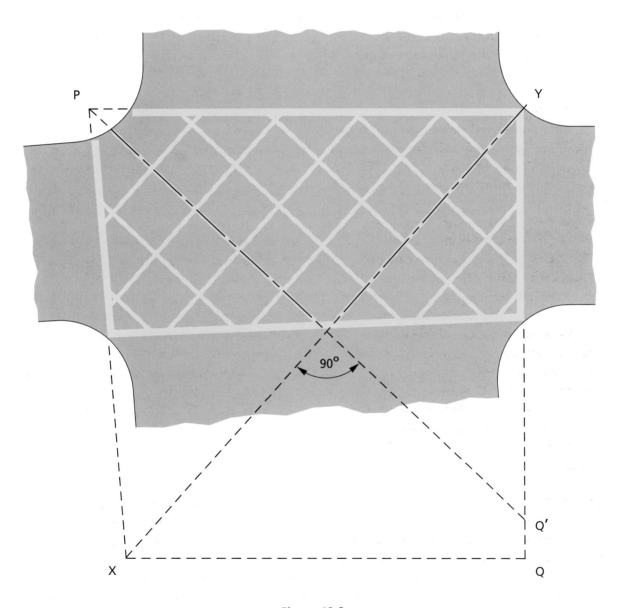

Figure 12-2

13 ARROWS AND LANE DESTINATIONS

LANE ARROWS

13.1 Direction arrows to diagram 1038 (see figure 13-1) should be used on the approach to busy multi-lane junctions to give drivers advance indication of the correct lane. The use of lane arrows at roundabouts is dealt with in paras 8.30 to 8.33, and at signal controlled junctions in para 9.9. Normally two arrows should be used in sequence in each lane, although sometimes three may be needed. Table 13-1 gives recommended arrow sizes and siting. Arrows or destination markings (see paras 13.4 to 13.6) should normally be located at least as far back from the junction as the longest peak hour traffic queue, but not in advance of a previous main junction as this might result in confusion. It can be helpful to locate arrows in conjunction with the advance direction signs.

13.2 The direction of each arrow head may be varied to suit the circumstances, but not more than two directions may be shown on any one arrow. The principal dimensions are indicated in figure 13-1; full details can be found on the working drawings (see para 1.17).

13.3 On two-lane approaches to junctions, the arrangement of arrows indicating the lanes for straight ahead, left turn and right turn will depend upon the relative traffic volumes making the movements, and on the site conditions. Where there is a heavy right turn movement, the straight ahead

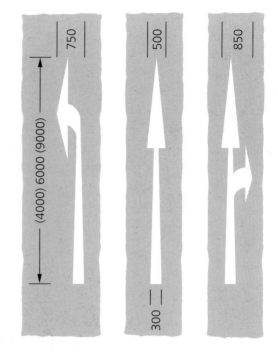

Diagram 1038

Figure 13-1

and left turn arrows should be combined in the near side lane. Similarly where there is a left filter arrow at a traffic signal installation, the filter lane should always be marked with the left arrow marking only, in order to exclude non-filtering traffic. Similar principles should be adopted where there are more than two lanes on an approach.

Table 13-1 Location of lane arrows

Speed limit (mph)	Arrow length (m)	Distance of first arrow from Stop/Give Way (m)	Distance of second arrow from first (m)	Distance of third arrow from second (m)
40 or less 50 or 60	4 6	15 to 25	30 to 50	30 to 50
70	9	Up to 1.5 times the above distances		

NOTE: The greater distances shown for the arrows should be used on roads subject to higher traffic speeds.

LANE DESTINATIONS

13.4 Worded lane destinations (diagram 1035, see figure 13-2) reinforcing the information shown on the advance direction signs may be marked on the carriageway on the approach to junctions. These will normally be used with lane destination arrows, although the latter may be omitted. In confirming which lane to use, the markings provide drivers with an alternative indication to the advance direction sign in the event of it being obscured by high

vehicles. Although abbreviations may be used, these must be understandable not only to local drivers, but also to those unfamiliar with the area. Abbreviations on the signs must be recognisable as the same destinations as those on the road, where fewer letters might need to be used.

13.5 Two sizes are prescribed for the legend, 1600 mm and 2800 mm. The smaller size is intended to be used when the speed limit is 40 mph or less, and the larger when it is more than 40 mph.

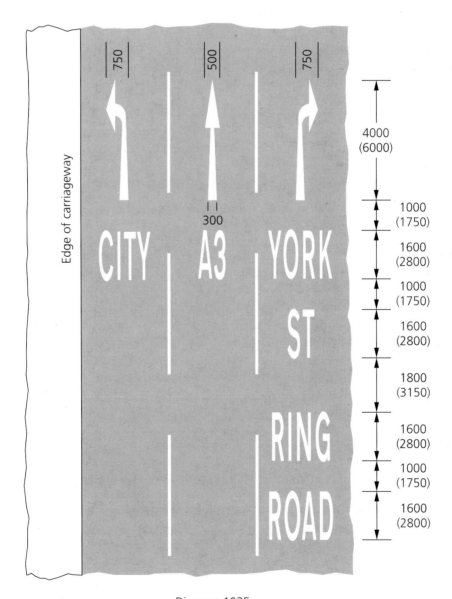

Diagram 1035

Figure 13-2

MANDATORY TURNS

13.6 Lane arrows supplemented with the legend TURN LEFT (see figure 13-3), TURN RIGHT and AHEAD ONLY are prescribed as diagrams 1036.1, 1036.2 and 1037.1 respectively. These versions may be used only where they indicate the effect of a statutory prohibition (direction 7). The markings are used to reinforce a green arrow traffic signal or a regulatory turn sign, e.g. entry into a one-way road where all traffic is required to turn in the same direction. The legend may be laid in a single line across two lanes or in two rows, as shown in figure 13-3.

GUIDANCE ARROWS

13.7 Lane markings may be laid in the junction where some guidance to traffic is considered to be helpful, although care should be taken that the meaning is clear to drivers on all approaches. Arrows to diagram 1038.1 (figure 13-4) may be used to indicate a route through a junction, or used in pairs to indicate that opposing right-turning traffic should pass near side to near side (see para 13.8). When used in pairs, a gap of at least one metre should be left between each arrow. Two lengths are prescribed for the arrow, 3025 mm or 4450 mm; normally the larger size will be appropriate, but at very restricted sites it may be necessary to use the smaller arrow. These arrows are identical to those that form part of the mini-roundabout marking to diagram 1003.4 (see figure 8-2) and shown on working drawing P1003.4 (see para 1.17).

13.8 Figure 13-5 shows the use of a pair of arrows to diagram 1038.1 at a signal controlled junction. Where a signal phase permits opposing right turns but no ahead movements from the right turn lanes, and there are no opposing dedicated lanes, use of the arrows to indicate that vehicles should pass near side to near side will help prevent conflict. If the number of right-turning vehicles is high, it would be of benefit to provide a dedicated right turn lane even if a separate signal stage is not provided.

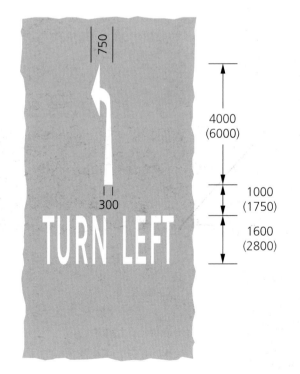
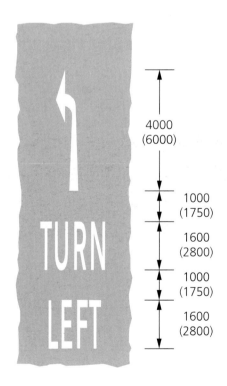

Diagram 1036.1

Figure 13-3

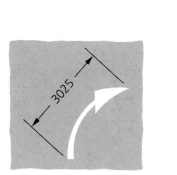 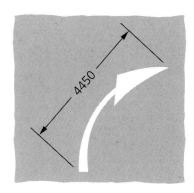

Diagram 1038.1 (alternative sizes)

Figure 13-4

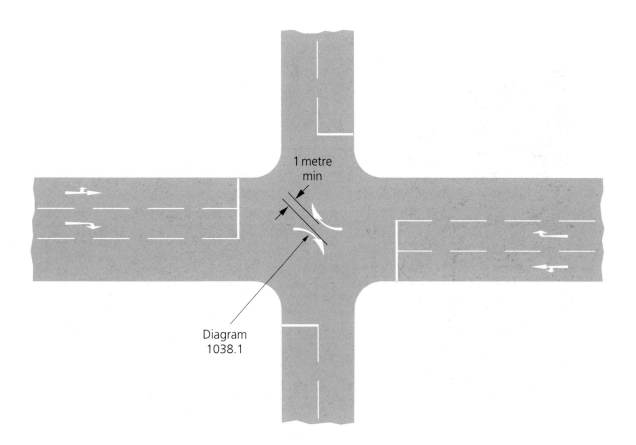

Figure 13-5

DEFLECTION ARROWS

13.9 Deflection arrows to diagram 1014 (see figure 13-6) are used in advance of:

(i) double white line markings to diagrams 1013.1 and 1013.3, to warn of the approaching restriction and to direct traffic to the correct side (see paras 5.13 to 5.16),

(ii) markings to diagrams 1040, 1040.3 and 1040.4, to warn of a hazard or change of direction and to indicate the side on which traffic should pass (see paras 4.50 and 4.53),

(iii) cycle or bus lane boundary markings to diagram 1049, to indicate the side on which other vehicles should pass them (see paras 16.6 and 17.7 respectively), and

(iv) arch bridges, in conjunction with the edge of carriageway marking to diagram 1010 and the marking to diagram 1024.1 (HIGH VEHS), to indicate the most suitable path for high vehicles (see paras 22.5 to 22.10).

The arrow may be reversed so that it points to the right in appropriate circumstances.

BIFURCATION ARROWS

13.10 These markings to diagram 1039 (see figure 13-7) should be provided at the commencement of deceleration lanes on the approach to junctions.

13.11 Bifurcation arrows serve to guide vehicles into the deceleration lane at its commencement, ensuring that the full length of the lane is used to slow down for the junction without impeding through vehicles on the main carriageway.

13.12 Three sizes are prescribed. The longest (32 m) is for use on motorways or high speed all-purpose dual carriageway roads, the medium (16 m) for use on other roads with a speed limit greater than 40 mph, and the shortest (8 m) elsewhere. It should be noted

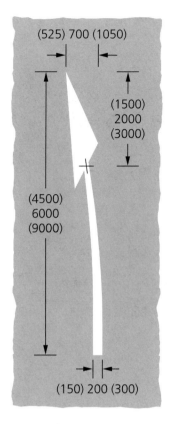

Diagram 1014

Figure 13-6

that the lateral distance between the tips of the arrow heads is 2100 mm for all three sizes of marking. For detailed dimensions, reference should be made to the working drawings (see para 1.17). The ahead arrow should be laid in the centre of the ahead lane; the turning arrow will then just encroach into the deceleration lane.

13.13 The arrow marking may be reversed to suit right turn movements into deceleration lanes in the central reservation of dual carriageways and dedicated right turn lanes on other roads. The arrow to diagram 1038 indicating a right turn (or ahead and right) must not be used in a through lane if it is not the lane from which traffic turns right.

13.14 Figure 13-8 indicates the location of the 32 m long arrow in relation to other markings. This may be used as a guide for other sizes of arrows; the aim should be to site the arrow shortly after the commencement of the deceleration lane, at a point where it has developed adequate width.

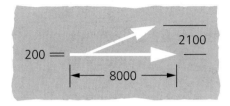
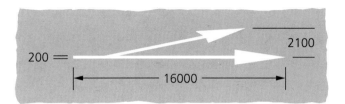

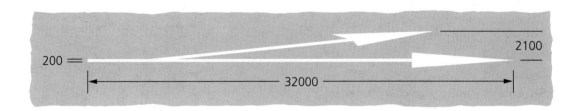

Diagram 1039

Figure 13-7

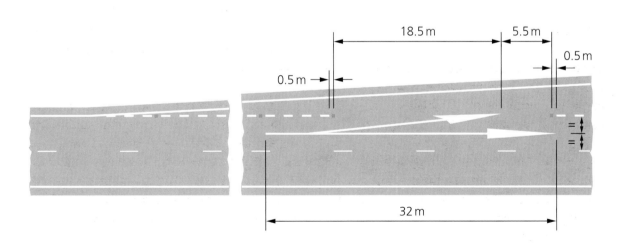

■ Green uni-directional reflecting road stud. Red, white and amber/red studs omitted for clarity.

Figure 13-8

14 TRAFFIC ISLANDS

GENERAL

14.1 The simplest means of marking approaches to traffic islands is to use inclined warning lines to diagram 1004/1004.1 as described in para 4.23. Where greater emphasis is required, hatched markings to diagram 1040 may be used (see paras 4.49 to 4.51). Details of the recommended minimum tapers are given in table 14-1 and guidance on the size of the markings in para 4.49.

14.2 It is important that the inclined warning line or the boundary line of a hatched marking guides traffic safely past the obstruction. Recommended clearances between the back of the line and the edge of a refuge are set out in para 4.23. The use of bi-directional road studs with diagram 1040 (or 1040.2) is not recommended, for the reasons explained in para 6.5.

14.3 Where traffic may pass on either side of an island, e.g. at a pedestrian refuge in a one-way street, a chevron marking to diagram 1041 is used (see also para 4.60).

14.4 A driver's view of an island may be obscured by other vehicles; the use of a white beacon will make its presence more conspicuous from a distance (see Chapter 4, section 23).

Table 14-1 Tapers on the approach to refuges

85 percentile speed (mph)	Preferred minimum taper	Absolute minimum taper
Up to 30	1 in 40	1 in 20
31 to 40	1 in 40	1 in 30
41 to 50	1 in 45	1 in 40
51 to 60	1 in 50	1 in 50

NOTES
1. The preferred minimum taper should be used wherever practicable; the absolute minimum should be used only where unavoidable.
2. See para 4.23 for details of minimum lateral clearance to refuge.

SUCCESSION OF ISLANDS

14.5 On four-lane single carriageway roads, pedestrian refuge islands may be provided to discourage excessive vehicle speeds and help pedestrians to cross.

14.6 The marking to diagram 1040.2 (see figure 14-1) may be provided as a more emphatic alternative to the use of the inclined warning markings described in para 4.23. The hatched marking discourages overtaking manoeuvres on the approach to each refuge.

14.7 Where access is required across the centre of the road to minor roads, the hatching may be omitted over a short length and replaced by a warning line to diagram 1004/1004.1 along the edge nearer the minor road. This will provide a narrow right turn lane. A right turn arrow to diagram 1038 may be used in this lane, but a bifurcation arrow (diagram 1039) at the entry point should not be used unless the turning lane is at least 2.5 m wide (see para 7.10). Marking in accordance with this paragraph helps to highlight the junction and give some protection to right-turning vehicles. If right turns into the minor road are prohibited, this can be emphasised by retaining the hatching even though vehicles may turn right out of the minor road. If the junction is with a major road and the right turn movements cannot be prohibited then a standard design of right turn lane will be necessary, possibly involving the dedication of the outside lane to right turners (see paras 7.2 to 7.12).

14.8 On narrower roads, the arrangement shown in figure 14-2 might be appropriate. However, the needs of cyclists must be considered; it can be intimidating if large vehicles have to pass very close in order to overtake. In addition, this layout will make passing slow vehicles difficult, and may cause problems if a vehicle breaks down. Waiting prohibitions may be needed adjacent to islands to prevent obstruction. Bus stops need to be carefully sited in relation to the island positions so as not to cause undue delays to other vehicles.

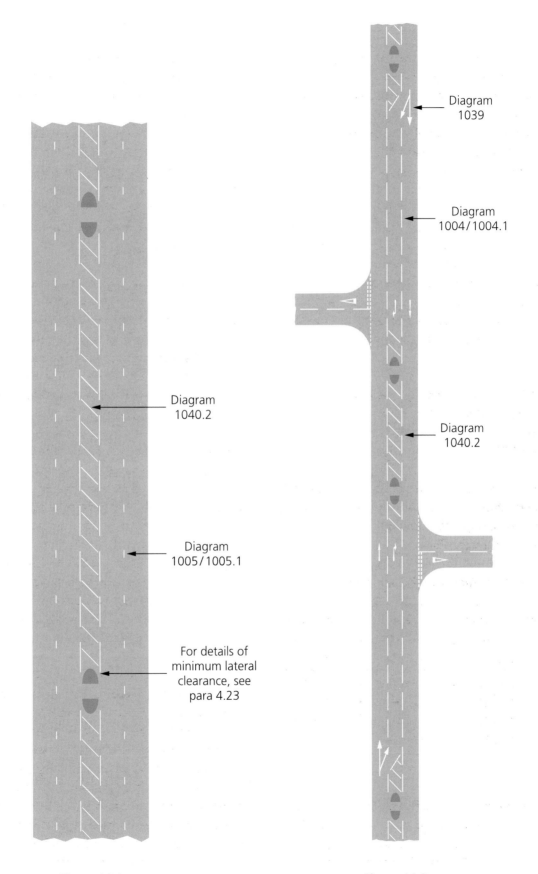

Figure 14-1 Figure 14-2

15 PEDESTRIAN CROSSINGS

GENERAL

15.1 Markings for Zebra, Pelican and Puffin crossings are prescribed in the Zebra, Pelican and Puffin Pedestrian Crossings Regulations and General Directions 1997 (the Pedestrian Crossings Regulations). Toucan and equestrian crossings are marked using diagrams 1001.3, 1055.1 and 1055.2 prescribed in the Traffic Signs Regulations and General Directions 2002. More detailed guidance on the provision of pedestrian crossings can be found in Local Transport Notes 1/95 (ISBN 0-11-551625-5) and 2/95 (ISBN 0-11-551626-3).

15.2 The width of a pedestrian crossing is determined by the pedestrian flow. An extra 0.5 m should be added to the minimum width of 2.4 m for each 125 pedestrians per hour above 600, averaged over the four peak hours, up to the statutory maximum width of 10 m.

15.3 Crossings should normally be positioned at right angles to the carriageway edge. Where this is impracticable, the Give Way or Stop line should as far as possible be at a right angle to the kerb, even if it is then not parallel to the edge of the crossing. This ensures that drivers do not violate the overtaking prohibition when stopping at the line alongside other vehicles.

ZEBRA CROSSINGS

15.4 The markings used to indicate a zebra crossing and its controlled areas (see figure 15-1) are:

(i) alternate black and white stripes (see paras 15.5 to 15.7),

(ii) Give Way lines lines (see para 15.8),

(iii) zig-zag lines including terminal lines (see paras 15.14 to 15.26), and

(iv) road studs (see paras 15.27 to 15.28).

15.5 Black and white stripes, between 2.4 m and 10 m long in the direction of travel (see para 15.2 for guidance on how to determine crossing width) are

laid across the full width of the carriageway. Road studs at Zebra crossings (see paras 15.27 and 15.28) are optional. Where used, they are placed not more than 155 mm from each end of the stripes. A post for mounting the yellow globe indicating the crossing must be placed at each end, normally on the side closest to approaching traffic.

15.6 The stripes immediately adjacent to the edge of the carriageway must be black and be not more than 1.3 m wide. All other stripes, both black and white, must be of equal width and not less than 500 mm nor more than 715 mm wide. The Pedestrian Crossings Regulations permit the minimum to be reduced to 380 mm and the maximum increased to 840 mm where an authority considers it necessary having regard to the road layout, e.g. stripes might be narrowed to increase the number on a narrow carriageway, or widened to reduce the number on a wide carriageway.

15.7 The white stripes may be illuminated with retroreflecting material. The carriageway surface may be used to represent the black stripes if it provides a reasonable contrast with the white.

15.8 The Give Way line consists of a single broken line comprising 500 mm marks and 500 mm gaps, and is 200 mm wide. It is normally sited between 1.1 m and 3 m from the edge of the stripes on the crossing, whether or not studs are used, and must extend across the full width of the carriageway. This 3 m limit may be increased up to 10 m if necessary (Schedule 1 para 11(3) of the Pedestrian Crossings Regulations).

PELICAN, PUFFIN AND TOUCAN CROSSINGS

15.9 The carriageway markings used to indicate the presence of these crossings (see figure 15-2) and their controlled areas are:

(i) Stop lines (see para 15.10),

(ii) zig-zag lines including terminal lines (see paras 15.14 to 15.26), and

(iii) road studs (see paras 15.27 to 15.28).

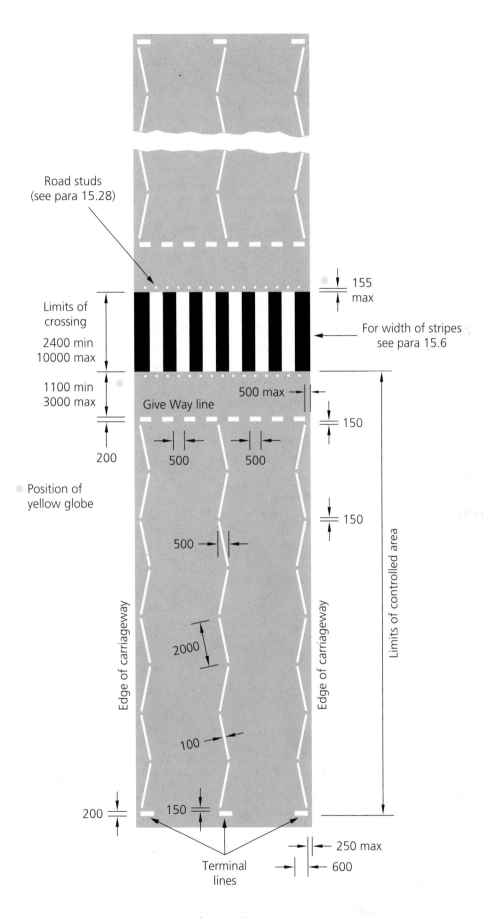

Road studs
(see para 15.28)

155 max

Limits of
crossing

2400 min
10000 max

For width of stripes
see para 15.6

1100 min
3000 max

500 max

Give Way line

150

500

500

200

150

Position of
yellow globe

500

Limits of controlled area

Edge of carriageway

2000

Edge of carriageway

100

200

150

250 max

600

Terminal
lines

Figure 15-1

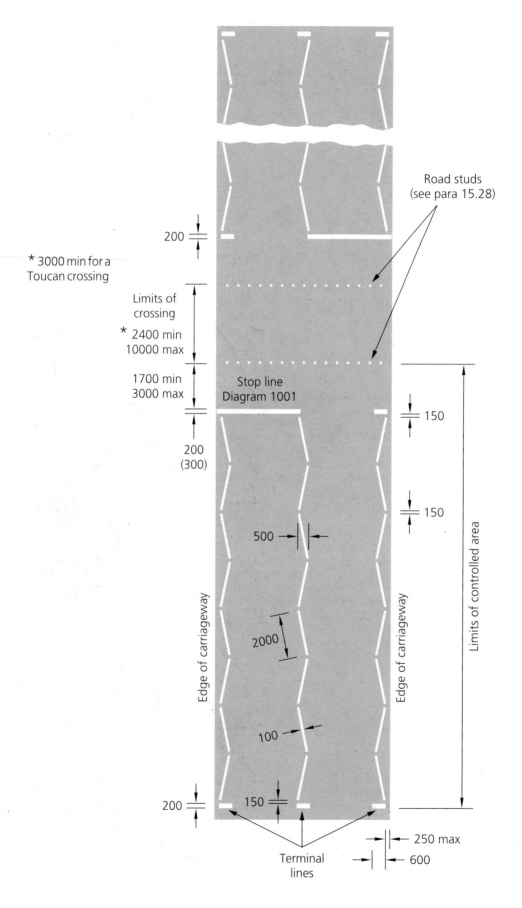

* 3000 min for a Toucan crossing

200

Limits of crossing

* 2400 min
10000 max

1700 min
3000 max

Stop line
Diagram 1001

200
(300)

Edge of carriageway

500

2000

100

200

150

Terminal lines

Road studs
(see para 15.28)

150

150

Edge of carriageway

Limits of controlled area

250 max

600

Figure 15-2

15.10 The Stop line to diagram 1001 indicates the position where traffic must stop when signalled to do so (see also para 3.7). The Stop line must be placed at least 1.7 m and normally not more than 3 m from the studs. This distance may be extended to a maximum of 10 m if necessary (Schedule 4 para 5(3) of the Pedestrian Crossings Regulations). On two-way roads the Stop line extends from the edge to the centre line, and on one-way roads across the full width.

EQUESTRIAN CROSSINGS

15.11 The markings at equestrian crossings (diagram 1055.2) are similar to those at Pelicans except that a second crossing place is provided for horses (see figure 15-4). Where no facility is required for other users, diagram 1055.1 is used.

15.12 The two crossing places are placed a minimum of 3 m apart to prevent pedestrians and cyclists being intimidated by horses. In order to deter drivers from stopping between the two crossings, the separation must be no greater than 5 m.

OTHER CROSSINGS

15.13 At traffic signal controlled junctions, markings to diagram 1055.1 may be used where cyclists cross under the control of signals, or where pedestrians cross whether or not they are themselves controlled by signals (see figures 9-1 and 9-2 and para 9.15).

ZIG-ZAG AND TERMINAL LINES

15.14 Zig-zag markings are used at Zebra, Pelican, Puffin, Toucan and equestrian crossings, the standard pattern comprising eight 2 m marks. They must not be used at crossings at signalled road junctions. The controlled area over which the Regulations apply extends from the limit of the crossing up to and including the terminal line. The length between the Give Way or Stop line and the terminal line is marked with zig-zags (see figures 15-1 and 15-2).

15.15 At Zebra crossings, a longitudinal zig-zag line should be laid on each side of the carriageway, with another in the centre. On carriageways up to 6 m in width, the latter may be replaced with a warning line to diagram 1004. On carriageways more than 6 m wide, a zig-zag line is always used as the centre line. On multi-lane approaches, the lane lines should also be replaced with zig-zag markings. Where there is a pedestrian refuge, a double row of zig-zag markings should be used in the centre.

15.16 The zig-zag marks are angled between two guide lines 500 mm apart. In standard and all longer patterns, the unit length of each zig-zag mark should be 2 m. They may be set out using a stencil positioned between the guide lines (see figure 15-3).

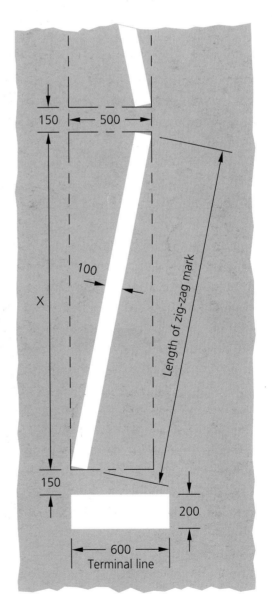

Figure 15-3

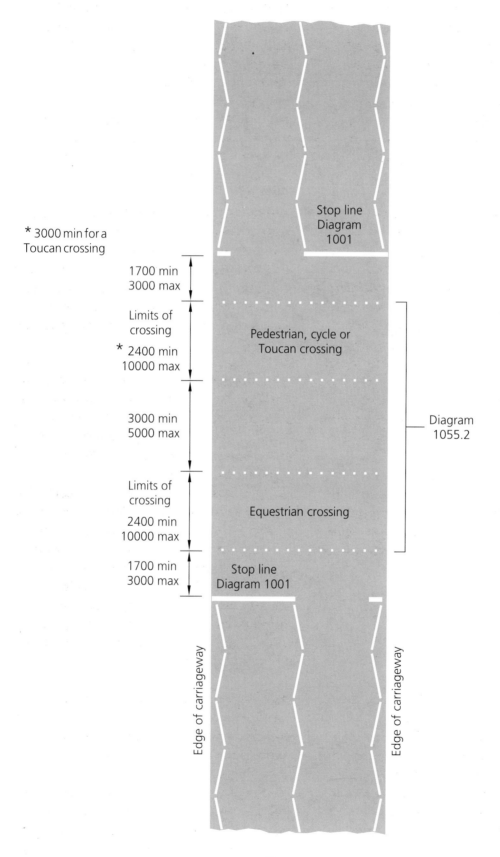

* 3000 min for a
Toucan crossing

1700 min
3000 max

Limits of
crossing

* 2400 min
10000 max

3000 min
5000 max

Limits of
crossing

2400 min
10000 max

1700 min
3000 max

Stop line
Diagram
1001

Pedestrian, cycle or
Toucan crossing

Equestrian crossing

Stop line
Diagram 1001

Diagram
1055.2

Edge of carriageway

Edge of carriageway

Figure 15-4

15.17 The length of the section of controlled area from the Give Way or Stop line to the terminal line inclusive (the marked controlled area, L in para 15.18) equals NX + (N+1)150 + Y + Z, where N = the number of zig-zag lines, X = the longitudinal limit of each mark (see figure 15-3), Y = the width of the Give Way or Stop line and Z = the width of the terminal line (all dimensions in millimetres). For a 2 m mark, X = 1.979 m, and the length L for eight 2 m marks is 17.585 m. Where a longer approach marking is required, e.g. where visibility is poor or the speed of traffic is high, the number of marks may be increased up to a maximum of 18. The aim should be to lay at least the standard pattern of eight 2 m marks on both sides of the crossing. Where site constraints prevent this, the length of the zig-zag marks may be varied to a minimum of 1 m and the number of marks reduced to a minimum of two. Zig-zag marks shorter than 2 m should be used only to indicate a controlled area of fewer than eight marks. Even then marks as near as possible to the maximum 2 m length should be provided, using a smaller number if necessary; each mark in each zig-zag line must be substantially the same length as the other marks in the same line.

Table 15-1 Numbers of zig-zags

Length available for the marked controlled area (m)	Recommended number of equal length zig-zag marks
2.750 - 4.500	2
4.500 - 6.500	3
6.500 - 9.000	4
9.000 - 11.000	5
11.000 - 13.000	6
13.000 - 15.500	7
15.500 - 17.585	8

NOTES

1. The length indicated in the first column consists of the controlled area detailed on figures 15-1 and 15-2, excluding the distance between the Stop or Give Way line and the limit of the crossing.
2. Crossings must not be laid with fewer than two zig-zag marks.
3. Where a length in the first column is common to two recommended numbers of marks, the lower number should be adopted.

15.18 For controlled area lengths between 2.750 m and 17.585 m, the appropriate number of zig-zag marks should be determined from table 15-1. The longitudinal limit of each mark (X in figure 15-3) is obtained from the formula $X = \dfrac{L - 350 - Y - 150N}{N}$

where L = the overall length available for marking, Y = the width of the Give Way or Stop line and N = the number of marks required from table 15-1 (all dimensions in millimetres).

15.19 Crossings on major roads should be located away from conflict points at uncontrolled junctions. The controlled area may extend across the mouth of a side road but it should never stop between the two projected kerb lines of the minor road. If this would otherwise occur, the zig-zag lines should be extended to the projection of the far kerb line of the side road.

15.20 Crossings on minor roads close to junctions will tend to restrict the layout of the controlled area markings. To preserve the effectiveness of a junction Give Way or Stop line, the terminal line of the zig-zag markings should not normally be less than 1 m from it. This distance may be reduced to 500 mm if necessary to enable the minimum pattern of markings to be laid. The controlled area should never extend beyond the nearer kerb line of the major road. It should be the aim to provide room for at least one vehicle turning into the minor road to wait at the crossing without obstructing traffic on the major road. More vehicles should be accommodated if there are large numbers turning. If signalled pedestrian crossings are sited too close to junctions, drivers might mistake a vehicular green signal for a priority signal over traffic on the major road.

15.21 Where part of a lay-by lies within the controlled area, the zig-zag markings should be laid along the edge of the main carriageway. However, the restrictions extend to the back of the lay-by.

15.22 Normally all zig-zag lines in a pattern should comprise the same number of marks. However, the Pedestrian Crossings Regulations allow for an exception to this rule to provide maximum coverage of the controlled area where the distance available for the marks on each side of the carriageway is unequal.

15.23 On dual carriageway roads and one-way streets, at least the standard pattern of eight 2 m marks should be laid on both sides of the crossing wherever possible (see also para 15.17).

15.24 Where a crossing is situated close to a roundabout, the markings should never be extended into the circulatory area, and they should be subject to the restrictions described in para 15.20.

15.25 The Pedestrian Crossings Regulations permit markings to diagrams 1029 (see paras 22.26 to 22.28 and diagram 6 in Schedule 4 of the Pedestrian Crossings Regulations) and 1062 to be used at or near a crossing. The use of diagram 1062 is described in paras 21.7 to 21.16. No other marking may be used within the controlled area, except hatched and chevron markings in the circumstances described in para 15.26.

15.26 The Pedestrian Crossings Regulations do not permit the use of central hatched or chevron markings within the controlled area of zebra crossings. Such markings may be used between a central double row of zig zags with Pelican, Puffin and Toucan crossings only in the following circumstances:

   (i)   diagram 1040 may be used on the approach to a central reservation (including pedestrian refuge) of a single crossing in a two-way road (Schedule 4, Part I, para 3(2) of the Pedestrian Crossings Regulations), and diagram 1041 in a one-way road (para 4(2)), and

   (ii)   diagram 1040.2 must be used on the approach to a staggered crossing (Schedule 4, Part I, para 3(3)).

ROAD STUDS

15.27 Road studs are arranged in two lines across the carriageway. They delineate the limits of the crossing, except at Zebra crossings where studs are optional and the limits are indicated by the stripes. At equestrian crossings, two crossing points are provided (see paras 15.11, 15.12 and figure 15-4).

15.28 Studs may be omitted at Zebra crossings, but must be provided at all other crossings. When provided, they must comply with the following requirements:

   (i)   they must be white, silver or light grey in colour and may be laid in road marking material or be conventional non-reflective road studs, in which case they must not project above the carriageway by more than 20 mm at their highest point nor more than 6 mm at their edges,

   (ii)   they must be either square or circular in shape. The sides of square or the diameter of circular studs must be not less than 95 mm nor more than 110 mm,

   (iii)   road marking material may be reflectorised, but retroreflecting road studs must not be used,

   (iv)   centres of studs in the same line must not be less than 250 mm apart nor more than 715 mm at a Zebra crossing, and not less than 500 mm nor more than 720 mm for other crossings. The centre of the nearest stud must be no more than 1300 mm from the edge of the carriageway, and

   (v)   the two lines of studs need not be at right angles to the edge of the carriageway, but they must form straight lines and, as far as practicable, be parallel to each other.

TRAFFIC CALMING

15.29 For guidance on the placing of crossings on road humps, see para 21.17.

GENERAL

16.1 Cycle facilities may take the form of cycle lanes (see paras 16.4 to 16.13) which run along the road and form part of the carriageway, and cycle tracks which are separate from the carriageway and meet up with it only to cross or join it (see paras 16.14 to 16.19). Cycle lanes may be mandatory, where other vehicles are excluded for at least part of the day (see paras 16.4 to 16.8), or advisory, where other vehicles may enter if necessary and when it is safe to do so (see paras 16.9 and 16.10). Coloured surfacing (see para 16.12) may be helpful.

16.2 Cycle lanes should be a minimum of 1.5 m wide. Widths less than this give cyclists very little room to manoeuvre around debris, surface defects or gulley gratings. Slightly narrower widths may nevertheless sometimes be helpful over short lengths, e.g. on the immediate approach to a junction. Where cycle flows are heavy, there may be advantages in increasing the width up to 2.0 m, but lanes wider than this are likely to be abused by other traffic.

16.3 For use on cycle lanes and tracks, the Regulations prescribe half-size variants of diagrams 1003 (Give Way line), 1009 (edge of carriageway) and 1023 (Give Way triangle), and small versions of the SLOW marking (diagram 1058.1) and the lane arrow (diagram 1059), see paras 16.23 to 16.25. The markings to diagrams 1040, 1040.2, 1041 and 1041.1 may have one of the boundary lines omitted when used alongside the line to diagram 1049 marking a cycle lane. Diagram 1057 (cycle symbol) is prescribed with alternative dimensions. The width of lane available and the required conspicuity of the marking will determine the appropriate size; the largest (1700 mm) is used with the advanced stop line (see paras 16.20 to 16.22). When used with a right turn arrow, the cycle symbol should be reversed to face right.

MANDATORY CYCLE LANES

16.4 Mandatory cycle lanes are parts of the carriageway which other vehicles must not enter except to pick up or set down passengers, or in case of emergency. They may be either with-flow (see

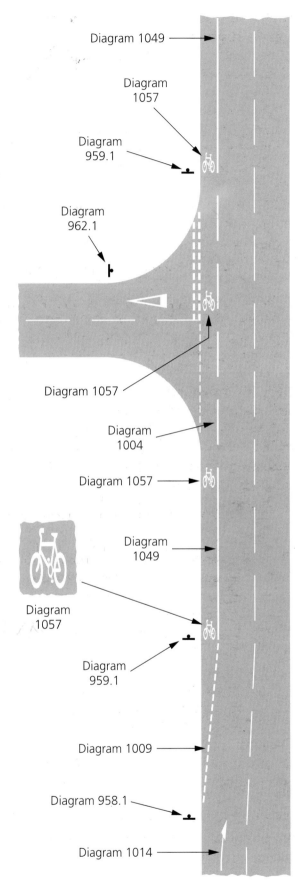

Figure 16-1

figure 16-1) or contra-flow (see figure 16-2). Contra-flow lanes apply for 24 hours, but with-flow lanes may operate for shorter periods, e.g. morning and evening peak hours.

16.5 With-flow mandatory cycle lanes are bounded by a 150 mm continuous white line to diagram 1049. The marking should be interrupted for the length of any bus stop marked by diagram 1025.1. At side road junctions the mandatory lane should change to an advisory one bordered by a 150 mm wide line to diagram 1004 or 1004.1; an additional cycle symbol to diagram 1057 should be placed in the lane in front of drivers emerging from the side road. The marking to diagram 1049 may be continued across private driveways; the traffic regulation order should provide exemption for access.

16.6 Regulation 4 requires the start of a cycle lane to be marked with a broken line to diagram 1009 (600 mm mark, 300 mm gap). If the speed limit is 40 mph or less, the 150 mm wide line is used, otherwise it should be 200 mm wide. As other traffic must not enter a mandatory cycle lane, adequate warning of the approach should be given by ensuring that the inclination of this line is no sharper than 1:10. Cycle symbol markings (diagram 1057) must be placed at the start of the lane and should be repeated after every break, as well as at suitable intervals on long uninterrupted lengths. A sign to diagram 958.1 should be used in advance of a mandatory cycle lane, together with an arrow to diagram 1014, and signs to diagram 959.1 must be used at intervals along its length.

16.7 A traffic regulation order will be required to prohibit other vehicles from using the lane (except for emergency and statutory purposes). The order should also prohibit waiting and loading during the operational hours of the lane. Yellow "no waiting" lines and kerb "no loading" marks are not necessary, unless it is required to prohibit waiting or loading for some period outside the operational hours of the cycle lane. In practice, many authorities nevertheless provide yellow lines and loading marks, even when the restrictions do not apply outside these hours, to encourage better compliance. Upright signs detailing the times of waiting and loading restrictions must then also be used.

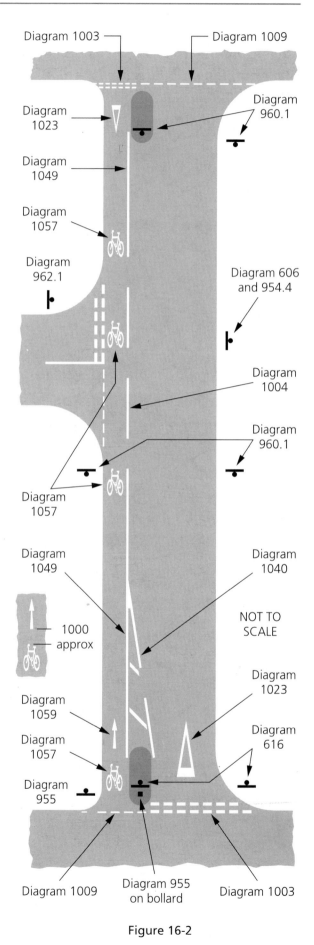

Figure 16-2

16.8 Contra-flow mandatory cycle lanes (see figure 16-2) are marked in a similar way to with-flow lanes, except that the marking to diagram 1009 at the commencement of the lane will be laid at right angles to it, as the lane normally starts at a junction. The sign to diagram 960.1 is used to warn traffic travelling in the opposite direction. Waiting and loading should be prohibited at all times to avoid the lane becoming obstructed and thereby putting cyclists into conflict with oncoming vehicles.

ADVISORY CYCLE LANES

16.9 Advisory cycle lanes are parts of the carriageway which other vehicles should not enter unless it is seen to be safe to do so. They should normally be with-flow (see figure 16-3), but may be contra-flow, in which case the signs would need to be specially authorised (see para 2.1). They should be bounded by a 100 mm wide warning line to diagram 1004 where the speed limit is 40 mph or less, or 1004.1 where it is greater than 40 mph. The line may be widened to 150 mm for greater emphasis, but in a two-way road it should never be wider than the centre line. For a contra-flow lane, the wider line should always be used.

16.10 The start of the cycle lane must be marked by a broken line to diagram 1009 (600 mm mark, 300 mm gap). If the speed limit is 40 mph or less, the 150 mm wide line is used, otherwise it should be 200 mm wide. As the lane is advisory, it is not essential for other vehicles to be deflected in advance of it. Angles between the line and the kerb of 30° to 45° are therefore often adequate, although longer taper lengths may be used. Cycle symbol markings (diagram 1057) and upright signs (diagram 967) must be placed at the start of the lane and after every break, as well as at suitable intervals on long uninterrupted lengths. Waiting and loading restrictions should be implemented to cover the times when the lane is most heavily used and should be indicated by the use of yellow lines, kerb markings and appropriate upright signs. An advisory cycle lane may be continued on the off side of a parking bay as shown in figure 16-3. Adequate clearance should be provided to allow for carelessly opened car doors.

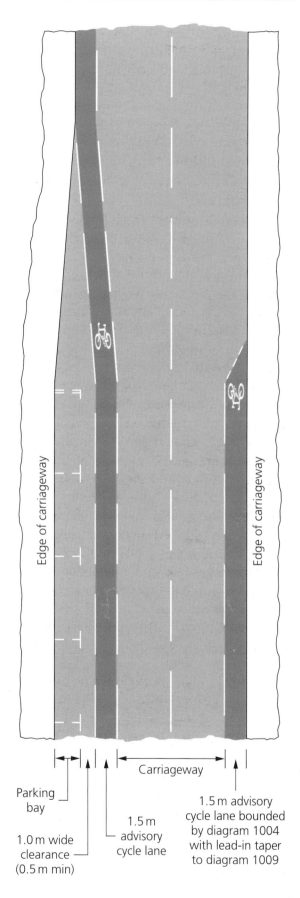

Figure 16-3

USE OF BUS LANES BY CYCLES

16.11 Cycles are normally allowed to use with-flow bus lanes; the BUS LANE marking to diagram 1048 is used. Upright signs to diagram 958 and 959 indicate that cycles may use the lane. Where cycles are permitted to use contra-flow bus lanes, markings to diagram 1048.1 BUS AND (cycle symbol) LANE must be used in place of diagram 1048. This marking must not be used in with-flow bus lanes.

COLOURED ROAD SURFACES

16.12 Cycle lanes and cycle reservoirs (see paras 16.20 to 16.22) may be surfaced in coloured material in order to demarcate them more emphatically and to discourage encroachment by motor vehicles. However, coloured surfacing has no legal significance; it is the prescribed traffic signs and road markings that establish the legal status of a cycle lane.

CYCLE LANES AT PEDESTRIAN CROSSINGS

16.13 Cycle lane markings must not be continued through the zig-zag area of a pedestrian crossing. Apart from the potentially confusing effect, they might also affect the legality of the marking of the crossing. If coloured surfacing is used for the cycle lane, this may be continued through the controlled area (although not through the crossing place itself), but the zig-zag marking must remain at the edge of the carriageway.

CYCLE TRACKS

16.14 A cycle track may be a physically segregated part of a highway, or form a separate highway entirely distinct from the road system. It may form a route for cycles only, a segregated route shared with pedestrians where cyclists and pedestrians use separate parts of the track, or an unsegregated route where both cyclists and pedestrians use the full width of the track.

16.15 Where a route is divided into separate parts for the use of cyclists and of pedestrians, segregation may be achieved using the continuous marking to diagram 1049 (150 mm width) or by the raised profile marking to diagram 1049.1 (see figure 16-4). The latter is more easily detected by blind and partially-sighted pedestrians. Alternatively, separation may be effected by the use of railings, a difference in level, or by the use of contrasting coloured surfaces (direction 33).

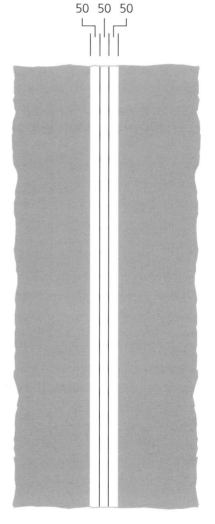

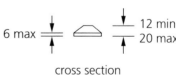

cross section

Diagram 1049.1

Figure 16-4

CYCLE TRACKS CROSSING ROADS

16.16 Except as described in para 3.25, a cycle track crossing a road will be the minor road at a priority junction, and marked as shown in figure 16-5, or be under signal control (see figure 16-6). The marking (sometimes known as "elephant's footprints") formerly shown on working drawing WBM 294 and in LTN 1/86 "Cyclists at Road Crossings and Junctions" should never be used to indicate an unsignalled crossing point. It is liable to cause confusion, and be misunderstood as giving cyclists priority over road traffic. At signalled crossings, the marking to diagram 1055.1 is usually adequate to indicate the crossing point for cyclists. However, if the route to be followed is not straightforward, the "elephant's footprints" marking might be helpful. As it is not prescribed, special authorisation must be sought from the Secretary of State (see para 2.1).

16.17 The 200 mm Stop line (diagram 1001) or the half-size variants of the Give Way markings (diagrams 1003 and if required 1023, see figure 16-5) together with the smaller size edge line to diagram 1009, should be used for a two-way cycle track at such locations. Where an unsegregated cycle track shared with pedestrians joins a road, the Stop line or Give Way marking should be used across the full width of the track and the cycle symbol to diagram 1057 should not be used.

16.18 If the cycle track crosses a dual carriageway road, the crossing should be staggered in the direction that turns cyclists to face oncoming traffic. The junction between the track and the main carriageway should be marked in accordance with the principles shown in figure 16-5 for a priority junction and figure 16-6 for a signalled junction.

16.19 Signs to diagram 963.1 (CYCLE TRACK LOOK BOTH WAYS) may be used to warn pedestrians of cyclists crossing the footway. The warning signs to diagram 950 or 543 as appropriate may be used to warn main road traffic of the crossing point.

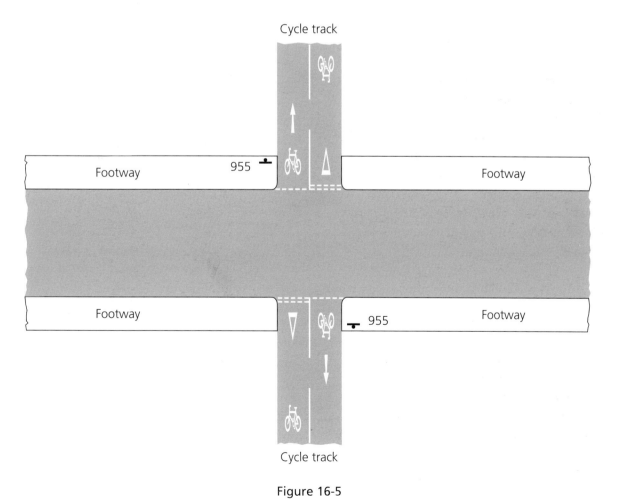

Figure 16-5

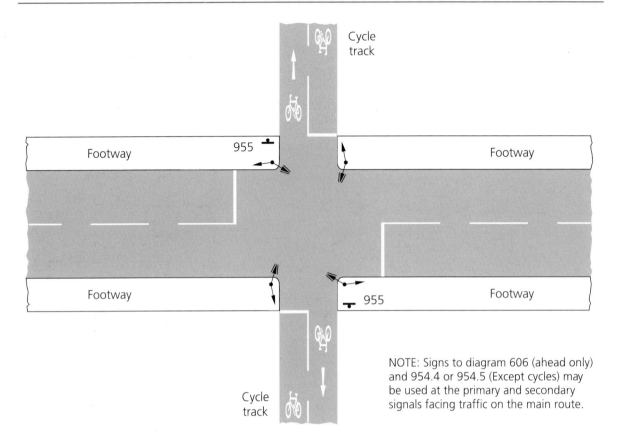

Footway

955

Cycle track

Footway

Footway

955

Cycle track

Footway

NOTE: Signs to diagram 606 (ahead only) and 954.4 or 954.5 (Except cycles) may be used at the primary and secondary signals facing traffic on the main route.

Figure 16-6

ADVANCED STOP LINES FOR CYCLISTS

16.20 Figure 16-7 shows typical layouts for an advanced stop line (diagram 1001.2) forming a reservoir space for cyclists at signalled junctions. They may not be used at level crossings or standalone signal-controlled crossings (for pedestrians, cyclists or equestrians).

16.21 Vehicles other than cycles must stop at the first line when signalled to do so. An advisory or mandatory cycle lane, preferably 1.5 m wide, must be provided to enable cyclists to enter the reservoir lawfully, i.e. without crossing the first stop line. The two Stop lines must be between 4 and 5 m apart; the area between them across the full width of the approach is available for cyclists to wait at the red light. This area and the approach lane may be highlighted using coloured surfacing (see also para 16.12). The Stop lines should be 200 mm or 300 mm wide (see para 3.7) and the boundary line should be the same width as the centre line of the road (this may be omitted where it is adjacent to a kerb).

16.22 Where there is a significant left turn flow of motor vehicles, but cyclists travel straight ahead, the approach cycle lane may be positioned centrally (see figure 16-7). The lane will be advisory, as it can then be indicated using markings to diagram 1057 and 1004 or 1004.1 without the need for an upright sign.

WORDED MARKINGS AND ARROWS

16.23 Figure 16-8 shows the reduced size SLOW marking to diagram 1058.1. The available lane width will determine the appropriate size.

16.24 The END marking (diagram 1058) is used only at the end of a route. It is not intended to be used at short breaks, nor where facilities continue in another form. It is prescribed in three sizes (750 x 705 mm, 1100 x 1035 mm and 1700 x 1600 mm). The available lane width will determine the appropriate size.

16.25 Figure 16-9 shows reduced size arrows to diagram 1059. The smaller size arrow should be used with the smallest size of cycle symbol.

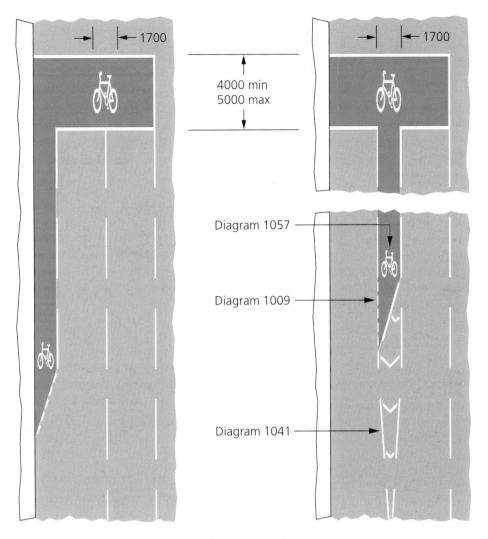

Diagram 1001.2

Figure 16-7

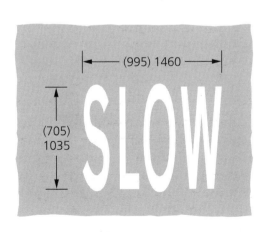

Diagram 1058.1

Figure 16-8

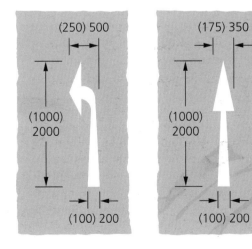

Diagram 1059

Figure 16-9

GENERAL

17.1 This section should be read in conjunction with LTN 1/97 "Keeping Buses Moving", available from the Stationery Office (ISBN 0-11-551914-9).

17.2 Bus lanes may be either with-flow (see paras 17.3 to 17.11) or contra-flow (see paras 17.12 to 17.15).

WITH-FLOW BUS LANES

17.3 The commonest form of bus priority measure is the with-flow bus lane, where buses travel in the same direction as traffic in the adjacent lane. It is normally used at the near side of the road. It may be used on the off side of a one-way road or dual carriageway, or may form the centre lane of a three-lane single carriageway road, but in such cases the markings and upright signs will need special authorisation (see para 2.1).

17.4 Figure 17-1 indicates a typical layout for a with-flow lane. Where roads are wide enough, the bus lane should be 4.25 m wide, with a minimum preferred width of 4 m. This allows buses to overtake cycles safely and reduces the likelihood of interference from general traffic in the adjacent lane. The minimum recommended width is 3 m.

17.5 The bus lane is separated from the rest of the carriageway by a continuous line to diagram 1049. The width of the line will be 250 or 300 mm depending upon site conditions, particularly the width of road available. The start of the lane is marked with a broken line to diagram 1010, the same width as the 1049 marking, and laid at a taper no sharper than 1:10. The lane should not start in such a position that the taper would extend across a side road junction.

17.6 The legend BUS LANE to diagram 1048 should be marked in the lane at its commencement. It should also appear after every side road junction on the same side of the road as the bus lane, and, in conjunction with signs to diagram 959, at intervals not exceeding 300 m along uninterrupted lengths of the lane. The marking to diagram 1048.1 BUS AND

(cycle symbol) LANE is prescribed specifically for use with contra-flow lanes if cycles are admitted (see para 17.12) and must not be used in with-flow lanes.

17.7 Deflection arrows to diagram 1014 should be placed 15 m and 30 m upstream of the start of the taper. The arrows should be 4.5 m long for speed limits up to 40 mph, 6 m for 50 or 60 mph, and 9 m for 70 mph. Traffic should be deflected to the right when the bus lane occupies the near side lane and to the left when it occupies the off side lane.

17.8 Where a bus lane passes a junction with a major left-turning flow into the side road, the line to diagram 1049 should be replaced with a broken line to diagram 1010 (see figure 17-1). The broken line should commence 30 m in advance of the junction, and have the same width as the bus lane line. It should be accompanied by the advisory direction arrow to diagram 1050 (varied to show a left turn). Detailed dimensions of the permitted variants are shown on the working drawing P 1050 (see para 1.17). At other junctions, the diagram 1049 marking should be terminated approximately 10 m before the junction (or at the junction if the minor road is one-way towards the major road, recommencing beyond the junction in combination with a marking to diagram 1010 (see figure 17-1).

17.9 With-flow bus lanes should normally be stopped short of the Stop line at traffic signal controlled junctions and the carriageway marked with an arrow to diagram 1050 (see figure 17-1). The purpose of this "set-back" is to ensure that full saturation flow can be sustained throughout the green period at traffic signals, thus minimising the delays to other traffic. It also facilitates, and makes safer, left turns at the junction. As a general guide, the length of the set-back (in metres) should normally be twice the minimum green time (in seconds), although it may be necessary to adjust this if there are special local site conditions or to take account of the variations in green time in active-response UTC systems. A with-flow bus lane should be brought up to the Stop line at a traffic signal only if a reduction in capacity of the junction is acceptable, if safe provision can be made for any left-turning traffic and if right-turning traffic can be accommodated in such a way that it does not restrict flow in the ahead lanes.

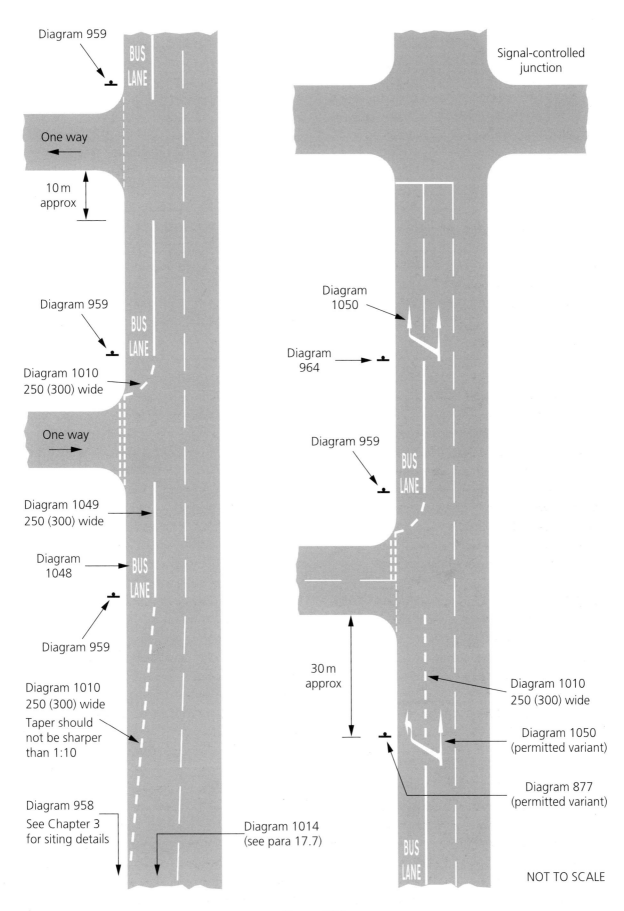

Diagram 959

One way

10 m approx

Diagram 959

Diagram 1010
250 (300) wide

One way

Diagram 1049
250 (300) wide

Diagram
1048

Diagram 959

Diagram 1010
250 (300) wide

Taper should
not be sharper
than 1:10

Diagram 958
See Chapter 3
for siting details

Diagram 1014
(see para 17.7)

Signal-controlled
junction

Diagram
1050

Diagram
964

Diagram 959

30 m
approx

Diagram 1010
250 (300) wide

Diagram 1050
(permitted variant)

Diagram 877
(permitted variant)

NOT TO SCALE

Figure 17-1

17.10 At roundabouts, a set-back should be provided to allow left-turning traffic to take the near side lane, and to ensure that the full width of the roundabout entry is available to all traffic at peak periods. The set-back distance should be determined on site, unless the roundabout is controlled by traffic signals in which case it should accord with the guidance given in para 17.9.

17.11 The order creating a bus lane will prohibit waiting during its operational hours. Yellow lines are necessary only if the waiting restrictions cover some period when the bus lane is not in operation. Loading and unloading is permitted unless it is specifically prohibited, in which case kerb marks and corresponding upright signs are always required.

CONTRA-FLOW BUS LANES

17.12 Contra-flow bus lanes allow buses to travel against the main direction of traffic flow in one-way streets. They are usually located so that buses travel with their near side to the kerb and are not normally used in other locations, particularly where stopping facilities are required. Cycles may be allowed to use them but difficulties may be experienced at junctions with vehicles turning across the lane, and with buses waiting at stops. They might themselves be a source of delay to buses, particularly in longer lanes.

17.13 Figure 17-2 indicates typical details for a contra-flow lane. The bus lane, which should be at least 3 m wide (4.0 to 4.25 m if cyclists are admitted), is separated from the rest of the carriageway by a continuous line to diagram 1049. The width of the line will be 250 or 300 mm depending upon site conditions, particularly the width of road available. The marking should be discontinued where it passes a traffic island, and angled at an appropriate taper (see table 14-1) to guide vehicles from each direction past the obstruction. Alternatively, the hatched marking to diagram 1040.2 may be used, with the bus lane line replacing one of the boundary lines as shown in figure 17-2.

17.14 At junctions on the near side, the lane should be discontinued, but unlike with-flow lanes a broken line is not necessary on the approach since there will be no left-turning traffic (except possibly buses). BUS LANE road markings to diagram 1048 (or 1048.1 if cycles are permitted to use the lane), together with direction arrows to diagram 1038, should appear at both ends of the lane, so that they can be read by drivers approaching the contra-flow lane. These markings should be repeated at every road junction and at intervals not exceeding 300 m along uninterrupted lengths.

17.15 BUS LANE LOOK LEFT/LOOK RIGHT signs to diagram 963 should be used at pedestrian crossing places. The road marking to diagram 1029 should also be used (see paras 22.26 to 22.28).

COLOURED ROAD SURFACES

17.16 Bus lanes may be surfaced in coloured material in order to demarcate them more emphatically and to discourage encroachment by other vehicles. However, coloured surfacing has no legal significance; it is the prescribed traffic signs and road markings which establish the legal status of a bus lane.

BUS LANES AT PEDESTRIAN CROSSINGS

17.17 Bus lane markings must not be continued through the controlled area of a pedestrian crossing (marked with zig-zags, see paras 15.14 to 15.26). The marking to diagram 1049 bounding the with-flow or contra-flow lane is not prescribed for use in such situations; it should be replaced with a row of zig-zags over the length of the controlled area on both sides of the crossing. If a coloured surface has been used for a bus lane (whether with-flow or contra-flow), this may be continued through the controlled area (although not through the crossing point itself).

BUS-ONLY STREETS AND BUS GATES

17.18 Where streets are reserved for the use of buses only, or buses and trams, or buses and cycles, the entry should be marked with diagram 1048.3 BUS ONLY, 1048.2 TRAM & BUS ONLY or 1048.4 BUS AND (cycle symbol) ONLY as appropriate.

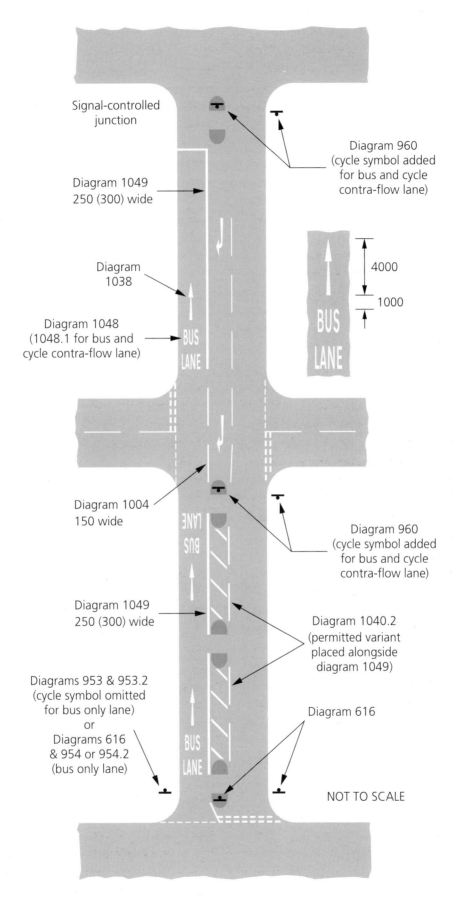

Signal-controlled junction

Diagram 1049
250 (300) wide

Diagram 1038

Diagram 1048
(1048.1 for bus and
cycle contra-flow lane)

Diagram 960
(cycle symbol added
for bus and cycle
contra-flow lane)

4000

1000

Diagram 1004
150 wide

Diagram 960
(cycle symbol added
for bus and cycle
contra-flow lane)

Diagram 1049
250 (300) wide

Diagram 1040.2
(permitted variant
placed alongside
diagram 1049)

Diagrams 953 & 953.2
(cycle symbol omitted
for bus only lane)
or
Diagrams 616
& 954 or 954.2
(bus only lane)

Diagram 616

NOT TO SCALE

Figure 17-2

17.19 Bus gates restrict entry to one end of a street to buses only. Beyond the gate, other vehicles may be encountered. The entrance to a bus gate should be marked in the same manner as a bus-only street.

BUS STOPS

17.20 The marking to diagram 1025.1 delineates the limits of a bus stop on the main carriageway (see figure 17-3), diagram 1025.3 a bus stop occupying part of a lay-by (see figure 17-4) and 1025.4 a bus stop occupying the whole of a lay-by (see figure 17-5). The yellow prohibition of stopping line in the marking prevents vehicles from stopping for at least part of the day, but must be used in conjunction with signs to diagram 974 or 975. The prohibition can be extended to 24 hours if appropriate by omitting the times from the sign. The line should be 200 mm wide where the speed limit is 60 mph or less, and 300 mm where it is 70 mph. In Northern Ireland, the Roads (Restriction of Waiting) Order (Northern Ireland) 1982 prohibits waiting at any time over the length of these markings. This would be effective (in Northern Ireland only) at times when the prohibition of stopping did not apply.

17.21 Both the worded marking and the broken line delineating the stopping area must be coloured yellow (except in Northern Ireland where it may be white). Only one size of marking is prescribed for a bus stop on the main carriageway. When the bus stop is in a lay-by (see figures 17-4 and 17-5), the width of the edge line should be 100 mm when the speed limit is 40 mph or less, 150 mm when it is 50 mph or 60 mph, and 200 mm when it is 70 mph. If the bus stop occupies only part of a lay-by (see figure 17-4), the broken edge line within the length of the bus stop would be coloured yellow, whilst that beyond it would be white.

17.22 Where the stop serves frequent or multiple services, or vehicles with different entrance positions, the length of the bay may be increased in increments of 2 m. The legend BUS STOP should be used once for every complete length of 12 m. Under-used stops of excessive length may result in enforcement difficulties.

17.23 The Regulations prescribe the alternative wording BUS STAND for use where buses are expected to wait longer than the period necessary to pick up or set down passengers (see Schedule 19 Part I).

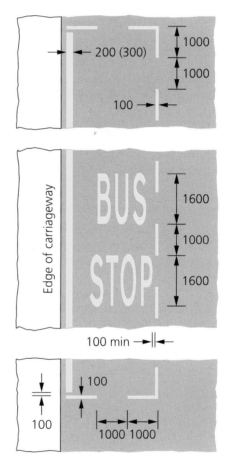

Diagram 1025.1

Figure 17-3

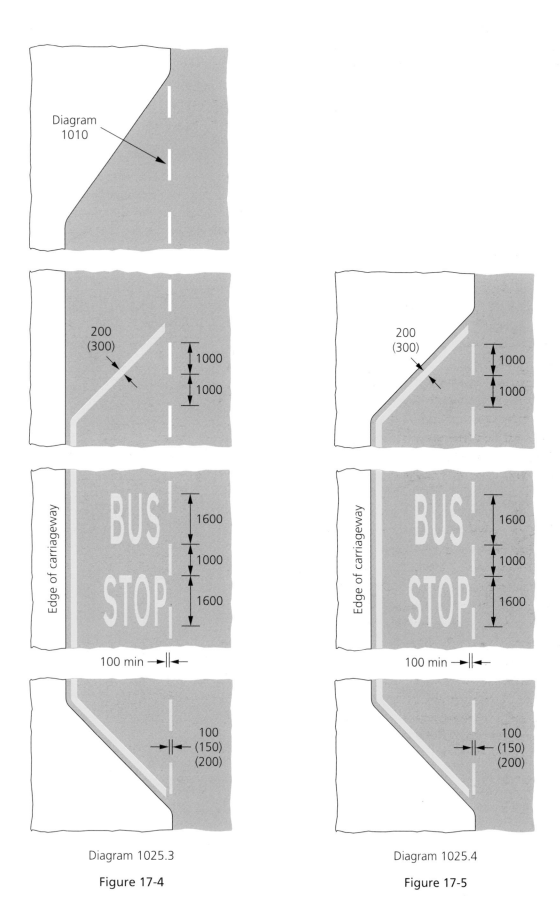

Diagram 1010

200 (300)

1000

1000

Edge of carriageway

BUS STOP

1600

1000

1600

100 min →‖←

100 (150) (200)

Diagram 1025.3

Figure 17-4

200 (300)

1000

1000

Edge of carriageway

BUS STOP

1600

1000

1600

100 min →‖←

100 (150) (200)

Diagram 1025.4

Figure 17-5

18 TRAM MARKINGS

GENERAL

18.1 The general principles for signing and marking tramways are set out in HM Railway Inspectorate's "Railway Safety Principles and Guidance, Part 2, Section G, Guidance on Tramways" published by the Health and Safety Executive (ISBN 0-7176-0951-0). The following paragraphs give more detailed guidance on the use of road markings for street-running tramways. Early contact should be made with the Inspectorate to discuss design issues.

18.2 Tramways may be categorised as follows:

(i)   integrated on-street tramways (see para 18.3) where the part of the highway occupied by the rails may be used by other vehicles or by pedestrians,

(ii) tram gates (see para 18.4), where only trams (and buses if permitted) travel along a short length of road that precedes an integrated on-street system,

(iii) segregated on-street tramways or tram-only streets (see paras 18.5 and 18.6) where the part of the highway occupied by rails may be crossed by pedestrians, but is not normally shared with other road users, or

(iv) off-street tramways (see para 18.7 to 18.10) where the alignment of the track is wholly separate from the highway.

INTEGRATED TRAMWAYS

18.3 Markings are used at junctions (see paras 18.11 to 18.15), at tram stops (see para 18.16 to 18.18) and to indicate the swept path of trams (see paras 18.19 to 18.23).

TRAM GATES

18.4 Access to an integrated route may be controlled by tram gates. These allow the passage of trams (and buses if permitted) using vertical signing to diagrams 953.1 and 953.2 in conjunction with the

marking to diagram 1048.2 TRAM ONLY or TRAM & BUS ONLY (see figure 18-1 and para 18.6). Although only these vehicles are allowed to pass through the gate, other vehicles may be encountered in the road ahead.

SEGREGATED TRAMWAYS

18.5 These may take the form of either a road that is reserved for trams only, or one in which other vehicles are allowed, but are physically separated from the tram route. In each case, buses may also be permitted to use the facility. No markings are currently prescribed for tram lanes and they would need to be specially authorised (see para 2.1).

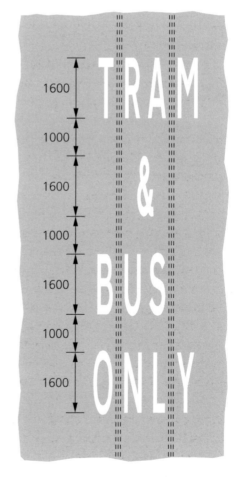

Diagram 1048.2

Figure 18-1

18.6 The worded marking to diagram 1048.2 TRAM ONLY or TRAM & BUS ONLY should be laid at the commencement of a segregated length of tramway and after any break where a road crosses the tramway. The marking should be laid so that no part of the lettering is on the running or check rails of the tram track. It should be arranged so that the words "TRAM" and "ONLY" are centred on the tracks with the first and last letters outside the running rails. The ampersand "&" is centred between the running rails and "BUS" needs to be offset, with the first letter outside the left hand running rail and the other two letters between the check rails (see figure 18-1).

OFF-STREET TRAMWAYS

18.7 Where a tramway diverges from an integrated system at a shallow angle onto a reserved length of track or to a tram stop, particular care needs to be taken to ensure that other drivers do not follow the tracks; this is particularly hazardous where it is the road that deviates leaving the tracks to carry straight on. Road markings are essential, in addition to appropriate vertical signing.

18.8 An edge line to diagram 1012.1 (see figure 18-2 and paras 4.31 to 4.38) should be provided, following the edge of the main carriageway at an angle across the tram tracks. The line should be discontinued where it crosses the running and check rails, but resumed in the space between the rails. This line should be supplemented by reflecting road studs of the appropriate colour (see para 6.9). Any stud laid within 2 m of the running rail should be of plastic construction. Physical measures to dissuade other vehicles from being driven along the tram track are recommended, e.g. the edge line may be supplemented by a low kerb painted alternately black and white, or by hostile paving.

18.9 Warning lines to diagrams 1004 or 1004.1 (see paras 4.12 to 4.26) should be laid in the centre of a single carriageway road, and in place of lane lines on multi-lane carriageways, following the line of the main carriageway.

18.10 A minimum of three arrows should be used to guide road vehicles past the divergence. The final arrow (3) should be positioned immediately after the point of divergence. The second and first arrows (2) and (1) should be placed before the point of divergence at distances equivalent to 1 and 3 seconds of travel respectively. These distances and the size of arrows that should be used are indicated in table 18-1. The appropriate type of arrow (diagram 1014 or 1038) depends upon the nature of the divergence, and is indicated in table 18-2 and figure 18-2. If the layout of the road is such that drivers might mistake arrow (1) or (2) as an indication to move to the next lane, then it should be omitted.

Table 18-1 Arrow size and location

Speed limit (mph)	Arrow length (m)	Distance from point of divergence (m)		
		Arrow number		
		1	2	3
30	4.5 (4)	40.5	13.5	0
40	4.5 (4)	54.0	18.0	0
50	6	67.5	22.5	0
60	6	81.0	27.0	0
70	9	94.5	31.5	0

NOTE: The smallest arrows to diagram 1014 and 1038 are 4.5 m and 4 m long respectively.

Table 18-2 Arrow type

Description of divergence	Figure	Arrow type		
		Arrow number		
		1	2	3
Tracks diverge from road	18-2a and 2b	1038	1038	1038
Road diverges to the left	18-2c	1014	1014	1014
Road diverges to the right	18-2d	1014	1014	1038

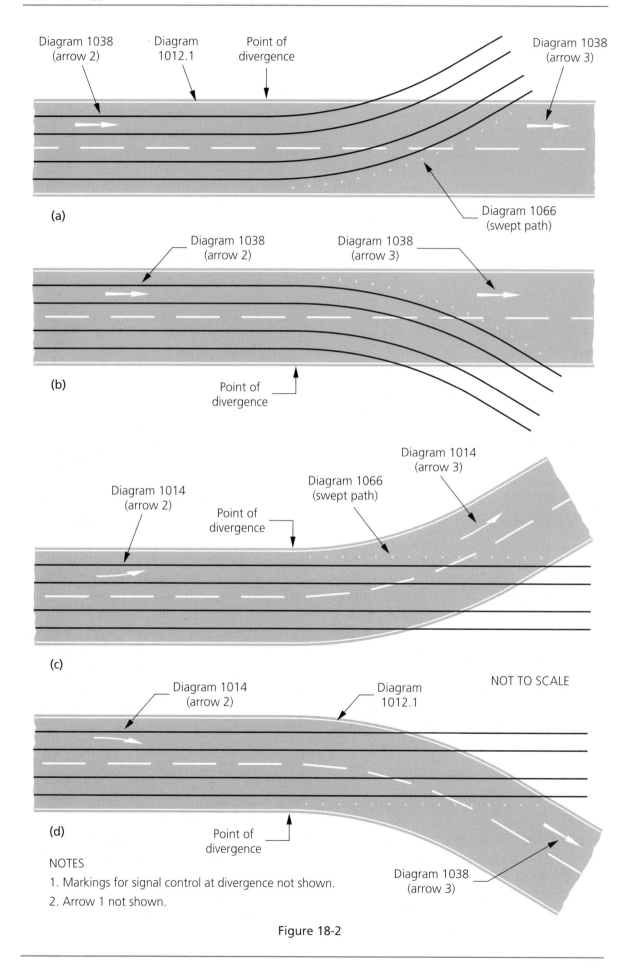

Figure 18-2

ROAD JUNCTIONS

18.11 Where a road is crossed by a segregated tramway which operates as a signalled railway, the junction should be signed and marked in the same way as a railway level crossing (see section 19) using the appropriate vertical tram signs.

18.12 Junctions with heavy traffic flows or restricted visibility (including those which would normally be signed with the diagram 601.1 STOP sign) should be controlled by traffic signals with the special white signals for tramcars (diagram 3013). Where the route is for tramcars only, the transverse tram Stop line to diagram 1001.1 (see figure 18-3) should be provided at right angles to the tracks, positioned a minimum of 1.5 m before the primary tram signal (2.5 m where practicable). If trams are running with other vehicles but not segregated from them with a physical refuge, the Stop line to diagram 1001 should be used from the kerb to the centre line. The tram Stop line may be used in addition, either just in front of or just beyond the Stop line; this might be necessary to facilitate swept paths or where primary tram and other traffic signals are not co-located. If the tram route is segregated from other traffic by a refuge, the respective Stop line is used on each side.

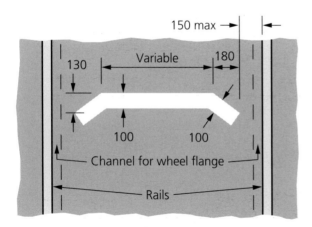

Diagram 1001.1

Figure 18-3

18.13 At priority junctions, roads carrying tramways should always be treated as the major road. Where the minor road would normally be provided with a vertical GIVE WAY sign (diagram 602), as well as the Give Way road markings (diagrams 1003 and 1023, see paras 3.14 to 3.23), this should be replaced with a STOP sign (diagram 601.1) and transverse Stop line (diagram 1002.1). The use of the STOP sign requires site approval by the Secretary of State (see para 2.1). At all other junctions with a road carrying a tramway, the minor road should have the transverse Give Way line (diagram 1003), the triangular marking (diagram 1023) and a GIVE WAY sign (diagram 602).

18.14 All transverse markings on roads joining a tram route should be placed outside the swept path of the tramcars (see paras 18.19 to 18.23).

18.15 Where yellow box markings (diagrams 1043 or 1044) are laid at a junction in accordance with the guidance in section 12, the yellow marking should not be laid on the running rails or check rails of the tramway (see also para 18.23).

TRAM STOPS

18.16 On modern tramways, tramcars stop at purpose-built platforms to help passengers to board. These are readily recognisable by other traffic and the raised platform makes it unattractive for other vehicles to park there, so there should be no need for clearway markings of the kind used at bus stops.

18.17 Where a tram stop platform is located on a length of road shared with other traffic, it is sometimes necessary for the raised platform to project into the carriageway to ensure that it is close enough to the tram for passengers to board. The end of the platform facing approaching traffic should be protected by kerbing or surface treatment, or by hatched road markings to diagram 1040.4 (see para 4.54) to guide other traffic away from the end of the platform. Hazard reflectors to diagrams 560 or 561 might also be necessary.

18.18 If the tram stop is in a lay-by or on a short length of road reserved for trams only, the TRAM ONLY variant of diagram 1048.2 (see para 18.6) may be used in conjunction with the sign to diagram 953.1 and the plate 953.2 to discourage other traffic from entering the tram stop area. Where the track leading to the tram stop diverges from the main carriageway at a shallow angle, the techniques described in paras 18.7 to 18.10 should be used.

SWEPT PATH MARKINGS

18.19 Tramcars are significantly wider than the tracks on which they run, and the overhang increases on curves. This "swept path" (which is the developed kinematic envelope plus a safety margin, typically 300 mm) may be indicated by the use of colour, texture or differences in level. It may also be shown using road markings to either diagram 1010 or 1066. The size of the safety margin should be agreed with the Railway Inspectorate. The swept path should be shown where it is not apparent from the carriageway or kerbs. Where there is on-street parking, it is essential that the swept path is visible to ensure that vehicles are not left in a position to obstruct trams.

18.20 Where it is important that drivers of both trams and other vehicles can readily identify the swept path, a marking to diagram 1010 is normally used. Where this might cause confusion to other drivers, e.g. where the track passes through a junction or the tramway diverges from the line of the carriageway, the marking to diagram 1066 may be used. The row of dots formed by this marking will be clear to tram drivers, but will not be readily observed by drivers of other vehicles who view them from a different angle. These marks should therefore be used where the swept path needs to be seen by tram drivers only.

18.21 The markings to diagram 1010 or 1066 should be laid along the edge of the swept path. The former marking should be 150 mm wide, whilst the marks to diagram 1066 should be between 55 mm and 100 mm in diameter and placed at 1.5 m centres, although a spacing of up to 2.5 m is permitted where necessary to avoid conflicting with other markings.

18.22 Where trams run together with other traffic on a two-way road, the centre line marking should be centrally located between the two swept paths. Where these are closely adjacent to each other, the marks next to the centre line should be omitted.

18.23 Where a tramway passes through a yellow box marking, the swept path should be indicated as shown in figure 18-4. The yellow markings should be terminated on either side of the swept path with a 200 mm wide boundary line. In these circumstances, the swept path is for the guidance of tram drivers only, so it is not necessary to continue the marking to diagram 1010 through the box.

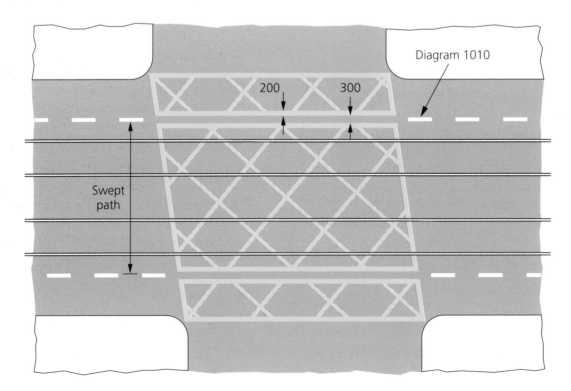

Figure 18-4

19 RAILWAY LEVEL CROSSINGS

GENERAL

19.1 Before a new level crossing is marked out or the markings at an existing crossing are modified, the railway operator and H M Railway Inspectorate must be consulted. Carriageway markings, road studs and other signing associated with level crossings are specified in the level crossing order (see also para 19.15). The normal arrangement is set out in detail in the Railway Inspectorate's publication "Railway Safety Principles and Guidance, Part 2, Section E, Guidance on Level Crossings" (ISBN 0-7176-0952-9). Unless otherwise indicated in that document, dimensions should be as specified in the relevant sections of this chapter. The Inspectorate's guidance details the following types of level crossing, explains when each should be used and includes drawings which show the road markings and vertical signs to be used with them:

    (i)   gated crossings operated by railway staff only,

    (ii)   manually controlled barrier crossing (MCB),

    (iii) automatic half barrier crossing (AHBC),

    (iv) automatic barrier crossing, locally monitored (ABCL),

    (v)   automatic open crossing, locally monitored (AOCL),

    (vi) open crossing (OC), and

    (vii) user-worked crossing (UWC).

Road markings are not normally provided at gated crossings operated only by railway staff, unless the crossing is also signalled. Where they are, they should conform to the following guidance.

TRANSVERSE MARKINGS

19.2 Transverse road markings should extend across the left hand half of each two-way carriageway, or across the full width of a carriageway which is either one-way or has no centre line marking.

19.3 Where road traffic light signals are installed, (MCBs, AHBCs, ABCLs and AOCLs) transverse Stop lines to diagram 1001 should be provided at right angles to the carriageway on each approach approximately 1 m before the primary traffic light signal. At AOCLs this should be increased to 2 m. The 300 mm size variant is recommended.

19.4 At OCs, Give Way lines to diagram 1003 should be provided at right angles to the carriageway on each approach to the crossing, but not less than 2 m from the running edge of the nearest rail. Give Way signs to diagram 602 and the triangular markings to diagram 1023 must also be used.

19.5 As UWCs are installed only where private roads cross the railway, carriageway markings are not normally used. However, where a STOP sign to diagram 601.1 is provided, a transverse Stop line to diagram 1002.1 and the word STOP to diagram 1022 should also be provided unless the road surface is unsuitable. If the private road is one to which the public has access, these markings must be used, utilising a short length of road surfacing if necessary.

19.6 At AHBCs, ABCLs, AOCLs and OCs, a pedestrian Give Way line to diagram 1003.2 should be provided across any footway. It should also be extended across the right hand side of a carriageway marked with a centre line, but this is not necessary where there are guard rails between the carriageway and the footway. It is not used at MCBs as the full width is controlled by barriers.

19.7 The pedestrian Give Way line should be at right angles to the carriageway. It should be located approximately 1 m on the approach side of any road traffic light signal, except at open crossings where it should be in line with the Give Way markings on the left hand side of the carriageway. No part of the line should be less than 2 m from the running edge of the nearest rail.

19.8 At obtuse skew crossings, the Give Way line for pedestrians should be provided in conjunction with a pedestrian signal. The end of this pedestrian line at the edge of the carriageway should be located not less than 2 m from the nearest rail (see figure 9 in the publication referred to in para 19.1).

LONGITUDINAL ROAD MARKINGS

19.9 A continuous line to diagram 1012.1 should be provided along each edge of the carriageway where the road passes over a level crossing. Line widths are detailed in table 4-5. A 100 mm wide line should also be provided along the back of each footway and, if separated from the main carriageway, along the front edge. The markings should be continued as necessary on each approach.

19.10 The type of centre line marking used generally depends on the width of the carriageway (see paras 19.11 to 19.13).

19.11 Where the width of the carriageway over the crossing is less than 5 m, centre line markings will not normally be provided.

19.12 Where the width of the carriageway over the crossing is 5 m or more, but less than 5.5 m, the centre of the carriageway between the Stop or Give Way lines should be marked with the appropriate longitudinal warning line to diagram 1004 where the speed limit is 40 mph or less, or 1004.1 where it is greater than 40 mph. The warning line should extend back from each Stop line for a distance equivalent to at least the minimum number of marks indicated in table 4-3, or for at least 6 m on each side of the crossing if beyond this distance the carriageway is less than 5 m in width.

19.13 Where the width of the carriageway at the crossing and on the immediate approaches is 5.5 m or more, the centre of the carriageway over the crossing should be marked with a double continuous line to diagram 1013.1A (see paras 19.16, 19.17 and figure 19-1). This should be continued along the approach to the crossing where justified by the normal visibility criteria for double white lines; at automatic half barrier crossings it should extend for at least 12 m back from the Stop line. Unless the double continuous line extends further back from each Stop line than the distance indicated in table 19-1, it should be preceded by a double white line to diagram 1013.1D, with the continuous line nearer to drivers approaching the crossing.

19.14 The minimum length of double white lines depends on the 85th percentile speed of private cars using the road, and on the general width of the carriageway (i.e. excluding any part of the crossing or approaches which may have been specially widened). Recommended overall lengths of the marking to diagram 1013.1A, or a combination of that marking and diagram 1013.1D, are shown in table 19-1. For roads having a carriageway more than 7.3 m wide the lengths in the table may be increased by up to 50%, but the double lines should not extend beyond the position of the sign to diagram 784.1, where this is used, unless a lay-by is provided.

19.15 At least one arrow to diagram 1014 must be provided on each approach to the double lines at crossings. This might be positioned outside the area covered by the level crossing order; if so, the traffic authority must ensure that it is provided. A second arrow is normally used on each approach (see paras 5.13 to 5.16 and table 5-1).

ROAD STUDS

19.16 The Regulations require double white lines to be accompanied by road studs (regulation 31(3)). A single row of white studs must be used, laid between the lines at nominal intervals of 4 m.

19.17 Any stud laid within 2 m of a running rail should be of plastic construction.

Table 19-1 Length of double white lines

85 percentile speed (mph)	Recommended length of double lines measured from the Stop line (m)
Up to 30	Up to 30
31 to 40	30 to 45
Over 40	45 to 60

YELLOW BOX MARKINGS

19.18 Yellow box markings to diagram 1045 may be provided only where specified in the level crossing order. They should be provided at AHBCs if the road traffic flow in any one direction exceeds the figures in table 19-2, but not normally at other types of crossing. Figure 19-1 shows a layout for a box marking at a single or double track railway crossing.

Table 19-2 Yellow box criterion

Overall width of carriageway (m)	Yellow box to be provided if vehicle numbers in any one hour in either direction exceed
5.0 to 5.9	500
6.0 to 7.4	600
7.5 and over	750

19.19 Where a long box is required (up to the 30 m maximum prescribed), the marking should be extended using additional diamond shaped units on the approach side and additional diagonal crosses on the trailing side of the crossing (see figure 19-2).

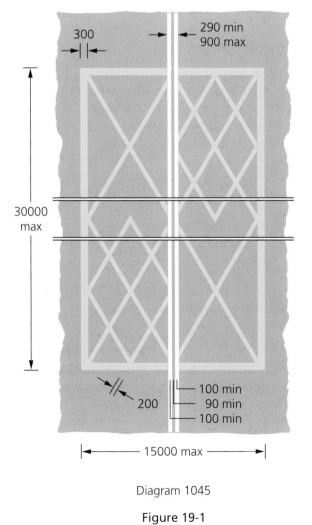

Diagram 1045

Figure 19-1

Figure 19-2

20 WAITING RESTRICTIONS

GENERAL

20.1 Markings indicate where waiting is prohibited (paras 20.3 to 20.6) or permitted (paras 20.11 to 20.27), and where loading is prohibited (paras 20.7 to 20.10). They are also used in conjunction with zonal signing (paras 20.29 to 20.33).

20.2 These markings must be used only to indicate the effect of a statutory provision (see direction 7) and (except for double yellow lines) must be used in conjunction with appropriate vertical signs (see direction 25). Further guidance will be found in Chapter 3. Adequate vertical signing is essential, so that drivers can readily establish the precise restrictions in force. Inadequately signed restrictions are likely to be legally unenforceable.

PROHIBITION OF WAITING MARKINGS

20.3 The markings consist of either a single or a double continuous yellow line laid at approximately 250 mm from the edge of the carriageway. The double line (diagram 1018.1) indicates that waiting of vehicles on that side of the road is prohibited at any time during a period of at least four consecutive months. The sign to diagram 637.3 is used only if the time period is at least four but less than twelve months. The single line (diagram 1017) indicates that the prohibition applies for some lesser time (of day, week or year). A transverse mark must be placed at each end of a line, where one type of line changes to another (see figure 20-1), where it abuts a bay marking or a zig-zag line and at a point where a vertical sign indicates the time period changes, but the road marking remains the same. The restriction imposed by these markings applies from the centre of the road to the highway boundary on the side of the road that the marking is laid (including any lay-bys).

20.4 Three widths are prescribed for yellow lines. The 75 mm size should be used on roads with a speed limit of 40 mph or less, and 100 mm on roads with a higher limit. In areas regarded as environmentally sensitive, the 50 mm wide line may be used. Alternative shades of yellow may be used (see para 23.18). The gap between double lines must in all cases be the same as the width of each line.

20.5 If restrictions are imposed in a lay-by, the lines to diagram 1017 or 1018.1 should be laid at the back of the lay-by and not along the continuation of the main carriageway edge. This should leave no room for doubt that restrictions apply in the lay-by.

20.6 Yellow waiting restriction lines must not be laid through a pedestrian crossing or its controlled area (the Zebra, Pelican and Puffin Pedestrian Crossings Regulations and General Directions 1997, regulation 9), nor at Toucan and equestrian crossings. See para 5.1 for guidance on the use of waiting restrictions with double white lines.

PROHIBITION OF LOADING MARKINGS

20.7 The markings consist of either a single or a double transverse mark on the kerb. The double mark (diagram 1020.1) indicates that loading or unloading of vehicles on that side of a length of

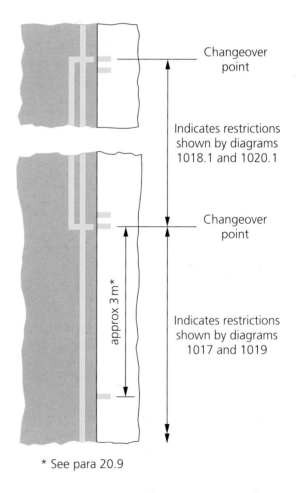

Changeover point

Indicates restrictions shown by diagrams 1018.1 and 1020.1

Changeover point

approx 3 m*

Indicates restrictions shown by diagrams 1017 and 1019

* See para 20.9

Figure 20-1

road is prohibited at any time during a period of at least four consecutive months. The single mark (diagram 1019) indicates that the prohibition applies for some lesser time (of day, week or year) than this. The restriction imposed by these markings applies from the centre of the road to the highway boundary on the side the marking is laid.

20.8 The kerb mark is 100 mm wide, with a gap of 100 mm between the lines of the double mark. The mark should be 250 mm long and may be extended down the kerb face. Where there is no raised kerb, the 300 mm mark should be used, positioned so that its nearer end is approximately 250 mm from the prohibition of waiting line.

20.9 The marks should be laid so that the first and last in the series correspond with the limits of the prohibition. Where two types of prohibition meet, the more restrictive marking should be placed at the point of change (see figure 20-1). The marks should be repeated at approximately 3 m intervals, but may be varied to between 2 m and 4 m to avoid a short length at the end. This spacing ensures that there will always be a mark alongside a stationary vehicle. A larger spacing would allow a vehicle to stop between the marks and a driver might claim that it was not clear that the prohibition extended between them.

20.10 The marks must not be laid at a pedestrian crossing, or within its controlled area.

Table 20-1 Bay marking details

Diagram No.	Alternative legends	Width of bay (mm)		Colour of marking
		At kerbside	In centre of road	
1028.2	TAXIS AMBULANCES POLICE	1800 min 2700 max	1800 min 2700 max	Yellow See note
1028.3	DISABLED BUSES LARGE OR SLOW VEHICLES ONLY LOADING ONLY No legend	2700 min (1800 min) 3600 max See para 20.13	3000 min 4200 max	White
1028.4	DOCTOR SOLO MOTORCYCLES ONLY SOLO M/CYCLES ONLY SOLO M/CS ONLY PERMIT HOLDERS ONLY No legend	1800 min 2700 max	1800 min 2700 max	White
1032	DOCTOR DISABLED LOADING ONLY No legend	1800 min 2700 max	Not prescribed	White
1033	DOCTOR No legend	2000 min 2500 max	Not prescribed	White
	DISABLED	3600		

NOTE: In Northern Ireland the colour of diagram 1028.2 may be varied to white.

PARKING BAYS

20.11 Parking bays may be marked parallel to the kerb, at an angle to it, wholly or partially on the footway, or in the centre of the road. They are prescribed as diagrams 1028.2, 1028.3, 1028.4, 1032 and 1033. Details are shown in table 20-1. Where the bay to diagram 1028.2 is allocated to different users at different times, a special direction should be sought from the Department to use no legend (see para 2.1).

20.12 The marking to diagram 1028.2 (figure 20-2) forms a single continuous bay with the legend TAXIS, AMBULANCES or POLICE as appropriate, marked outside the bay. The marking is coloured yellow (in Northern Ireland this may be varied to white). It is laid

either at the road edge or in the centre of the road and may be extended to any length to accord with the traffic order. The legend should be repeated at intervals of about 12 m and marked on both sides when used in the centre of the road. Where stopping by other vehicles is prohibited, the sign to diagram 650.1 is used together with the yellow prohibitory line from diagram 1025.1 (see para 17.20). Otherwise the prohibition of waiting sign to diagram 650.2 is used. In both cases a traffic regulation order is required.

20.13 The marking to diagram 1028.3 (see figure 20-3) forms a wide bay, designed for use by vehicles displaying a disabled person's badge, by buses or by large vehicles. It is accompanied by the upright sign to diagram 639.1B, 660 (varied to

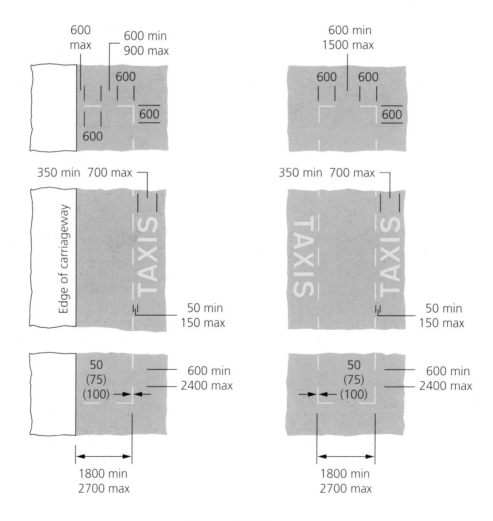

Diagram 1028.2

Figure 20-2

"Large or slow vehicles only"), 660.4 ("Loading only"), 661A ("Disabled badge holders only"), 661.1, 786 ("PARK HERE AND USE PHONE AT CROSSING"), 801 (when used with 804.1), or 969. The bay is white in colour and may be accompanied by the legend BUSES, DISABLED, LARGE OR SLOW VEHICLES ONLY or LOADING ONLY, marked outside the bay. It may be placed at the road edge or in the centre of the road. When marking a space for disabled users, the word DISABLED may be omitted, e.g. in streets with block paving, although use of the legend will help badge holders identify parking places more easily. It is recommended that all disabled bays in a locality are treated in the same way to avoid confusion. The bay may be extended to any length to accord with

the traffic order. The legend should be repeated at intervals of about 12 m and marked on both sides when used in the centre of the road. If the road is too narrow to permit traffic (especially fire engines) to pass a 2700 mm wide DISABLED bay, the bay width may be reduced, subject to an absolute minimum of 1800 mm. When the width is 2700 mm or less, the transverse marking will be as in diagram 1028.4.

20.14 The LARGE OR SLOW VEHICLES ONLY variant of diagram 1028.3 may be used with the sign to diagram 660, similarly varied, at level crossings where drivers are required to stop and telephone before crossing. It may also be used to designate places for large vehicles awaiting police escort.

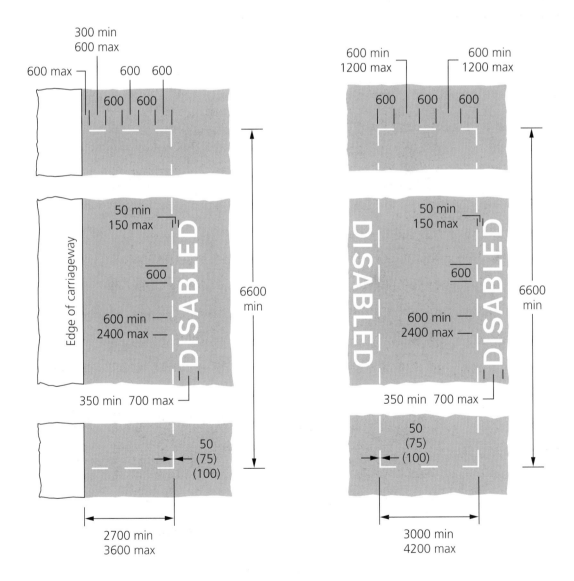

Diagram 1028.3

Figure 20-3

20.15 The marking to diagram 1028.4 (figure 20-4) indicates a designated parking place used for limited waiting, for permit holders, for a particular class of vehicle, or for payment parking. It forms a single bay coloured white and may be placed at the edge or in the centre of the road. Where provided for in the order, it may be laid partly or wholly on the footway (see para 20.23) and extended to any length. The legend DOCTOR may be omitted or varied to SOLO MOTORCYCLES ONLY, SOLO M/CYCLES ONLY, SOLO M/CS ONLY or PERMIT HOLDERS ONLY, and should be repeated at intervals of about 12 m.

20.16 The marking to diagram 1032 (figure 20-5) is used to divide a length of road into individual parking places, each end of a series of parking places being marked as a double line. The dividing marks between two adjacent spaces may be omitted to form a single long bay with a maximum length of 13.2 m.

The words DOCTOR, DISABLED or LOADING ONLY may be added in the manner shown in diagram 1028.4 (figure 20-4). The marking was originally for use only when charges were made for parking. However, it may now also be used to mark individual bays for free limited waiting. Where charges are discontinued, it will therefore no longer be necessary to change the bay markings.

20.17 The angled bays indicated in diagram 1033 (figure 20-6) may be used both where charges are made (i.e. pay and display, meter, permit, voucher or disc parking) and where parking is free. The angle between the markings and the carriageway edge may be varied to suit the available road width. When not at right angles, the bays should be angled so that drivers are required to reverse into them. This is safer than reversing out, when visibility might be restricted by adjacent parked vehicles.

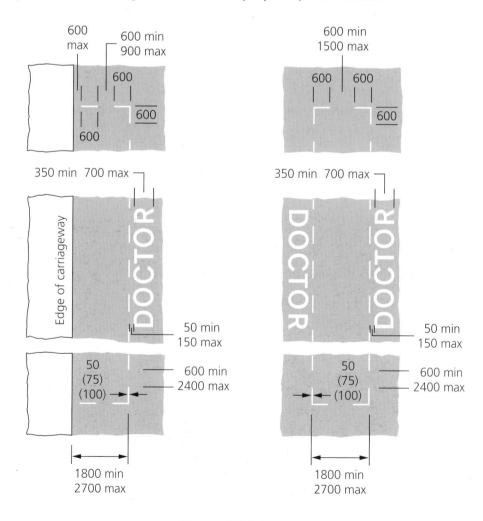

Diagram 1028.4

Figure 20-4

20.18 One or more of the angled parking places may be reserved for the use of disabled badge holders. Each such bay is then widened to 3.6 m; the legend DISABLED may be added to each bay to help identify it. Standard width bays may indicate DOCTOR. The limit of the row of parking bays must be marked with the double terminal mark shown in diagram 1033; this is omitted where the limit is delineated by a raised kerb. The extended marks shown alongside the DISABLED legend are used to mark the limits of the DISABLED bay (or DOCTOR when so marked).

MARKING OF BAYS

20.19 The normal width of the lines outlining parking bays is 50 mm. This may be varied to 75 mm for greater emphasis or to reduce maintenance, or to 100 mm to accommodate the use of paving blocks in block-paved areas. Any legend should be marked outside the bay and with the correct orientation to be read by a passing driver (see figure 20-7). The transverse line may be omitted where the marking is placed in a layby or where the end of the bay is delineated by a raised kerb (see figure 20-7).

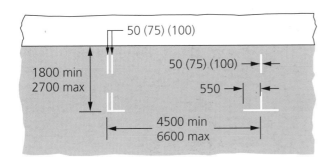 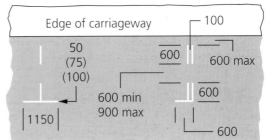

Diagram 1032

Figure 20-5

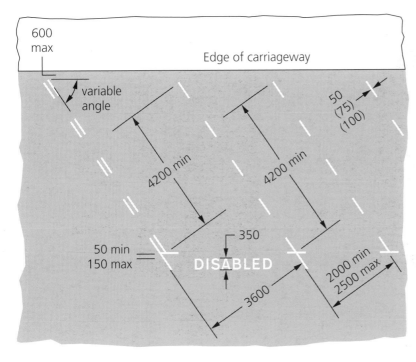 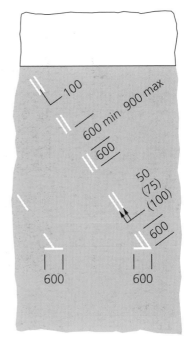

Diagram 1033

Figure 20-6

20.20 A bay laid adjacent to the road edge should be designed so that neither it nor the associated legend overlaps the centre line road marking. A centre line should not be interrupted alongside bay markings. If conditions allow, it may be moved away from the geometric centre of the carriageway to permit traffic to pass a row of parked vehicles without crossing the centre line. Lane lines should not be interrupted but may also be realigned if practicable.

20.21 If adjacent bays for different uses would be of different widths, the greatest width should be adopted for all (where permitted by the Regulations) to avoid a potentially confusing stepped edge.

20.22 Where a taxi bay (diagram 1028.2) is sited next to a bay coloured white, it will be necessary to use the single yellow terminal line and the white terminal line (double white if the white bay is diagram 1032). There should be a gap of 100 mm between the two markings. However, when changing between 1028.3, 1028.4 and 1032, the transverse white line (or one such line of diagram 1032) should be treated as common to both markings if they are identical in size and colour (see figure 20-7 for examples).

20.23 Where a bay is laid partly on the footway and partly on the carriageway, it should be to the pattern shown in the right hand diagram in figure 20-4. Where a bay is marked wholly on the footway, it should be the reverse of the pattern shown in the left hand diagram in figure 20-4 and adjacent to the kerb. Any legend should be laid only on the carriageway side of the marking (see figure 20-7).

SHARED AND PART TIME BAYS

20.24 It is sometimes necessary for bays to be available for two or more different uses at different times of the day, or for bays to be used for parts of the day only. Guidance on this is given below.

20.25 If waiting (or loading) restrictions apply at times when the marking to diagram 1028.2 is not operating, the normal yellow lines or kerb marks should be used in addition to the bay marking. When the "no stopping" variant is used (see para 20.12

and direction 22(3)(a)) the yellow line to diagram 1017 is omitted. Kerb marks are still required if loading is prohibited outside these times.

20.26 Where waiting is prohibited at certain times (e.g. peak hours) and limited waiting, or waiting by specified classes of user, permitted at other times, a white bay marking (diagram 1028.3, 1028.4, 1032 or 1033 as appropriate) should be used with a single yellow line to diagram 1017 continued through the bay. Where loading is prohibited, the kerb markings to diagram 1019 or 1020.1 must also be used. An upright sign to diagram 639.1B should be provided. The bottom parts of the sign may be varied to diagrams 660, 660.3, 660.4, 660.5, 661A, 661.2A, 661.3A or 662 if appropriate.

20.27 If the upper part of diagram 639.1B is varied to diagram 650.2 (no waiting except taxis or other designated vehicles), the white bay marking appropriate to the lower panel is used. The yellow bay marking to diagram 1028.2 normally associated with diagram 650.2 cannot be used in these circumstances, so the presence of the waiting restrictions shown in the upper part of the sign is indicated with a single yellow line to diagram 1017.

20.28 Yellow waiting or loading restriction markings are discontinued through markings to diagrams 1025.1, 1025.3, 1025.4 and 1028.2 (when used with diagram 650.1), as they already incorporate a continuous yellow edge line, (see direction 22(3)(a)).

CONTROLLED PARKING ZONE

20.29 This category includes meter, disc, ticket, pay and display and voucher parking, and any combination of these. Yellow lines (diagram 1017 or 1018.1) and, if appropriate, kerb marks (diagram 1019 or 1020.1) must be laid throughout the zone, other than at parking places (or bus stop clearways or mandatory school entrance markings which apply throughout the zone hours). Parking places must be marked with white bay road markings (diagrams 1028.3, 1028.4, 1032 or 1033). Vertical signs in the zone are required only if restrictions differ from the terminal sign.

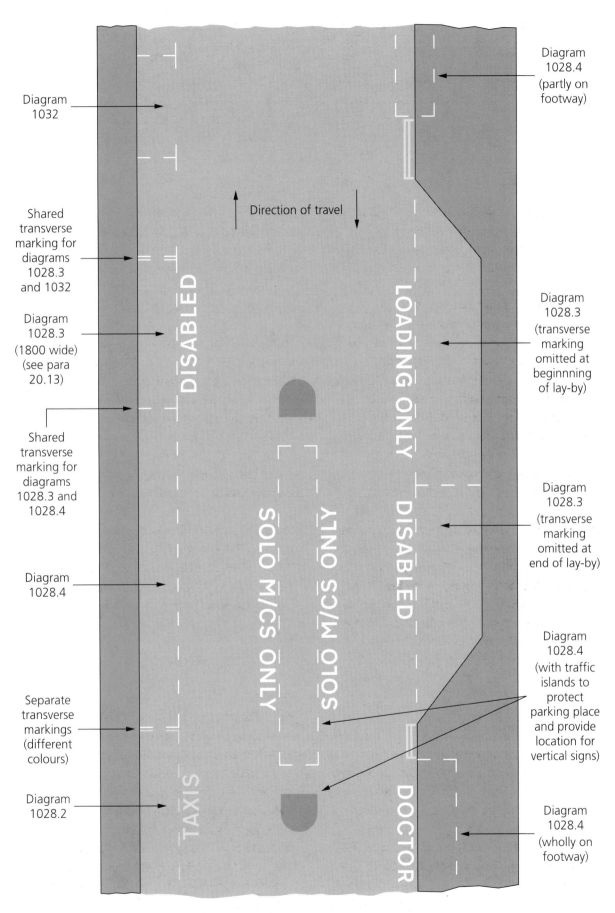

Diagram 1032

Shared transverse marking for diagrams 1028.3 and 1032

Diagram 1028.3 (1800 wide) (see para 20.13)

Shared transverse marking for diagrams 1028.3 and 1028.4

Diagram 1028.4

Separate transverse markings (different colours)

Diagram 1028.2

Diagram 1028.4 (partly on footway)

Diagram 1028.3 (transverse marking omitted at beginnning of lay-by)

Diagram 1028.3 (transverse marking omitted at end of lay-by)

Diagram 1028.4 (with traffic islands to protect parking place and provide location for vertical signs)

Diagram 1028.4 (wholly on footway)

Direction of travel

DISABLED

LOADING ONLY

DISABLED

SOLO M/CS ONLY

SOLO M/CS ONLY

TAXIS

DOCTOR

Figure 20-7

PEDESTRIAN ZONE

20.30 Yellow lines (and kerb marks) must be used unless the conditions in direction 24(4) are met (see para 20.31) or a special direction has been issued to omit them (see para 20.32). Parking or loading bays are not normally provided, but see para 20.32(iii).

20.31 The conditions under which direction 24(4) permits the omission of yellow lines and kerb markings are where:

(i) the entry of vehicles is restricted at the same time as the waiting restrictions apply,

(ii) the footway and carriageway are not separately defined (i.e. the whole road width is paved over without change of level or material), and

(iii) the waiting restrictions apply uniformly throughout the zone.

20.32 It may be possible to issue a special direction (see para 2.1) to allow yellow lines and kerb marks to be omitted in other circumstances, for example:

(i) where the road surface is not paved but vehicles are not likely to be parked outside the times at which vehicle entry is restricted,

(ii) where the road surface is at one level, but different colours or textures of surfacing are used to distinguish the carriageway from the footway, and the other requirements of direction 24(4) are met, or

(iii) where parking and loading bays, bus stops or taxi ranks are provided within the zone, but waiting restrictions are otherwise uniform. The bays will need standard markings, or to be delineated by bollards, planters or other street furniture.

RESTRICTED ZONE

20.33 Restricted zones generally use vertical signs to restrict parking, with no yellow line markings. They are signed using a specially authorised variant of diagram 663 with the legend "Restricted ZONE" and the words "Except in signed bays" added where appropriate. White bay markings (diagrams 1028.3 or 1028.4) or yellow bus stop or taxi markings (diagrams 1025.1, 1025.3, 1025.4 or 1028.2) will be used if required. They need not be used if the bays are physically delineated by kerbs, bollards, planters or other street furniture.

LORRY AND BUS PARKING BAN ZONE

20.34 Where it is desired to ban parking by large vehicles for part of the day in residential areas, lorry or bus parking ban zones may be introduced. Such zones are effected using upright signs to diagrams 640.2A and 665, without the use of road markings.

CYCLE AND BUS LANES

20.35 The use of yellow lines in cycle lanes is dealt with in para 16.7, and in bus lanes in para 17.11.

21 TRAFFIC CALMING

INTRODUCTION

21.1 This section is not intended to be a detailed description of traffic calming techniques, but a guide to the markings used with such schemes.

21.2 Advice on marking the following is given in the paragraphs indicated:

    (i)   speed limit roundels (paras 21.4to 21.6),

    (ii)   road humps (paras 21.7 to 21.12),

    (iii) speed cushions (paras 21.13 to 21.15),

    (iv) thumps (para 21.16),

    (v)   humped crossings (para 21.17),

    (vi) build-outs (paras 21.18 to 21.21),

    (vii) chicanes and pinch points (paras 21.22 to 21.25), and

    (viii) gateways (paras 21.26 to 21.28).

Guidance on the warning signs provided for road humps can be found in Chapter 4.

21.3 In 20mph zones signed with diagram 674, road markings are not required on road humps, speed cushions or thumps; however they may be used if the traffic authority considers them appropriate. Hump markings are always required where a 20mph speed limit is signed using diagram 670.

SPEED LIMIT ROUNDEL

21.4 An indication of the speed limit may be placed on the carriageway using the marking prescribed in diagram 1065. The marking is varied to show the speed limit in force and elongated in the direction of travel to compensate for the foreshortening effect (see figure 21-1). It must not be used in association with an advisory speed limit.

21.5 The marking may be used where a speed limit changes, or as a repeater in conjunction with upright signing. On roads where there is a 20mph speed limit, elongated roundels may be used in conjunction with the vertical 20mph repeaters. Neither signs nor road markings may be used as repeaters to indicate a 30mph speed limit on roads with street lighting.

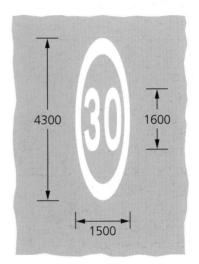

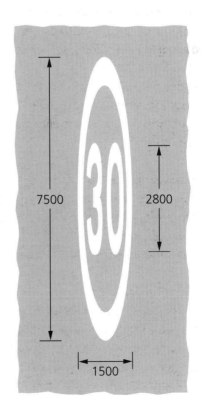

Diagram 1065

Figure 21-1

21.6 The larger marking is used at the start of a speed limit if approaching traffic is subject to a limit higher than 40 mph, otherwise the smaller size is used. The size of repeater markings should be appropriate to the speed indicated, with the smaller roundel being used where the limit is 40 mph or less.

MARKINGS ON ROAD HUMPS

21.7 The 2002 Regulations changed the way that road hump markings are prescribed. Diagrams 1060, 1060.1, 1061 and 1061.1 in the 1994 Regulations were replaced by the triangular marking to diagram 1062 (see figure 21-2). Other prescribed markings are used on humps as required.

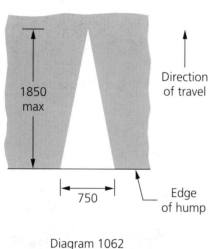

Diagram 1062

Figure 21-2

21.8 Road hump profiles will generally be either round or flat-topped with ramps. Figure 21-3a shows a typical layout of markings on a round hump, and figure 21-3b on a road hump with tapered ends. Figure 21-3c indicates the markings used on flat-topped humps. Tapered ends are not used at flat-topped humps provided to help pedestrians cross the road (see para 21.17 for guidance on locating pedestrian crossings on road humps).

21.9 The triangular marking to diagram 1062 is used on the approach side of a hump. It should extend from the edge of the hump to the highest point (or for a maximum distance of 1850 mm if this is less).

On flat-topped humps, the triangle marking should extend for the length of the ramp, if this is less than 1850 mm. Two triangular marks should be used in each lane; in one-way roads they should be placed only on the approach side of a road hump.

21.10 At a hump that is 5 m or more in width, unless at a Zebra or signalled crossing (see also para 21.17), the top of the hump must be marked with a line to diagram 1004 (see paras 4.12 to 4.26). This should be used on the approach to as well as over a hump, to separate the opposing flows of traffic in a two-way road. Where more than one lane is available to traffic proceeding in the same direction in either a one-way or a two-way road, the lanes should be separated by the marking to diagram 1004, and two triangular markings to diagram 1062 should be used in each lane. Care should be taken to ensure that it is evident which line marks the division between opposing streams of traffic, e.g. by widening the centre line marking to 150 mm.

21.11 Where a road hump has tapered ends which terminate within 300 mm of the kerb, edge line markings to diagram 1012.1 (see paras 4.31 to 4.38) or yellow lines to diagram 1017 or 1018.1 must be used, deflected over the hump to guide vehicles away from the taper (direction 18(1)). These should normally extend at least 6 m beyond the hump.

21.12 In some cases it might prove helpful to provide a cycle lane bypass between the kerb and the taper of a road hump. Where possible this should be in the form of a mandatory cycle lane, so that other vehicles do not enter the area. The width of the cycle lane should be between 750 mm and 1000 mm.

MARKINGS ON SPEED CUSHIONS

21.13 A speed cushion is a form of road hump occupying only part of the traffic lane in which it is installed (see figure 21-3d).

21.14 A single triangular marking to diagram 1062 should be used on the approach ramp of each cushion. Where vehicles from both directions might be driven over the same cushion, the triangular marking should be used on both approach ramps.

Optional

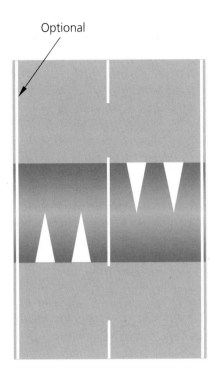

Figure 21-3a

Diagram 1012.1, 1017
or 1018.1 must be used

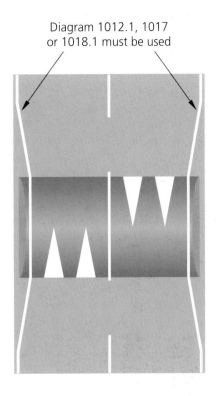

Figure 21-3b

Optional

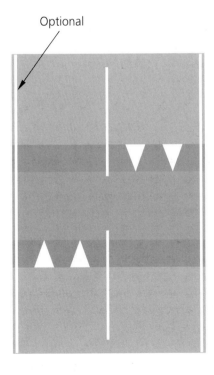

Figure 21-3c

Optional

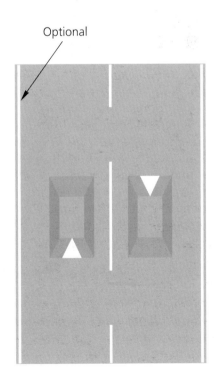

Figure 21-3d

Figure 21-4a

Figure 21-4b

21.15 There is no marking prescribed for delineating the edges of a speed cushion as a warning to pedestrians. It is recommended that cushions be constructed in material which contrasts with the road surface. If a cushion is placed in the centre of a carriageway and may be approached by vehicles from either direction, hatched markings to diagram 1040 or 1040.2 may be used on both approaches.

MARKINGS ON THUMPS

21.16 A thump is a road hump which is between 900 and 1500 mm long (in the direction of travel). No markings are necessary if it is constructed from yellow reflective material. Where non-reflective material is used, it should not be coloured yellow, but should normally incorporate four (with a minimum of two) markings to diagram 1062 on each side of the thump in line with the approach lane. The markings should extend from the edge to the top of the thump and, in a one-way road, they should be applied across the full width of the carriageway. Edge of carriageway markings may be continued over the thump if desired.

HUMPED CROSSINGS

21.17 Pelican, Zebra, Puffin and Toucan crossings may be placed on flat-topped kerb-to-kerb humps (see figure 21-4). Humps may extend into the controlled areas, but the crossing must remain centred upon the hump. The detailed regulatory requirements are set out in regulation 4 of the Highways (Road Humps) Regulations 1999.

BUILD-OUTS

21.18 A build-out is a feature that extends into the carriageway on one side of the road only. It may be constructed integrally with the footway, or a gap may be left for drainage, or for cyclists where it is considered that they would be at risk of being squeezed by passing vehicles. The approach to a build-out should normally be marked using diagram 1040.4, with the taper specified in table 14-1. Where

there is parking immediately preceding the taper, the markings described in para 21.20 may be used. An edge line to diagram 1012.1 may be added. Any yellow waiting restriction lines should follow the line of the kerbs around the build-out and not be stopped either side of a chicane or pinch point.

21.19 If it is intended to assign priority to traffic from one direction, Give Way and triangular markings (diagrams 1003 and 1023) may be provided, supplemented if required by signs to diagrams 615 with 615.1 and 811 with 811.1 (see also para 3.24). Note that it is not lawful to require traffic from both directions to give way. The build-out is normally used on the side of the carriageway leading into a traffic-calmed section and priority given to vehicles travelling in the opposite direction. The Railway Inspectorate should be consulted at an early stage if such an installation is planned near a level crossing.

21.20 A series of build-outs along one side of a road can be used to provide sheltered parking places. Projecting the build-out beyond parked cars also enables pedestrians waiting to cross to see and be seen. Diagram 1010 should be used to delineate the edge of the carriageway available for through traffic unless the parking is controlled by a traffic regulation order, in which case the appropriate bay marking is used (see paras 20.11 to 20.28).

21.21 If a gap is provided for cycles, it should be marked with the cycle symbol, diagram 1057, and the appropriate vertical sign. Such a gap may, however, inconvenience pedestrians using the build-out as a crossing place.

CHICANES AND PINCH POINTS

21.22 A chicane is a narrowing of the carriageway formed by locating build-outs alternately on each side of the road. Pinch points are formed by the construction of build-outs opposite one another; they may be useful at crossing places, whether controlled or not, to reduce the width of carriageway to be crossed. The approaches to chicanes and pinch points should be marked using diagram 1040.4 with the tapers specified in table 14-1.

21.23 A centre line road marking to diagram 1004 should not normally be used between the build-outs of a chicane or pinch point unless the width of each traffic lane so formed would be 3 m or more.

21.24 Any yellow waiting restriction lines should follow the line of the kerb around the build-out (see para 21.18).

21.25 Chicanes are not normally appropriate places for pedestrians to cross the road as the attention of drivers is likely to be concentrated on negotiating the features. Pedestrians should not therefore be encouraged to cross at such locations, whether by the installation of formal crossings or dropped kerbs. If, however, pedestrians are likely to cross at a chicane, the design should ensure that they can be seen clearly and that they can cross the road safely.

GATEWAYS

21.26 Gateways can be provided to indicate places where the road changes in character, e.g. where a rural road enters a town or village. They must not prevent the passage of any vehicle unless there is an appropriate traffic regulation order.

21.27 Edge lines and hatched markings can be used to make the carriageway appear narrower than it is, whilst still allowing larger vehicles to overrun these areas if necessary. The effect will be increased if a central refuge island is provided together with hatched markings, but care must be taken not to increase hazards to cyclists. In rural areas, the width of some farm vehicles needs to be considered and care should be taken not to prevent these or other wide vehicles from passing. If there is insufficient space to accommodate a physical island, a ghost island formed by markings alone can be helpful.

21.28 Edge lines and hatched markings should taper in accordance with table 14-1.

22 WORDED AND DIAGRAMMATIC MARKINGS

GENERAL

22.1 This section contains guidance on the use of the following markings:

    (i)   SLOW (paras 22.2 to 22.4),

    (ii)   HIGH VEHICLES (paras 22.5 to 22.10),

    (iii) KEEP CLEAR (paras 22.11 to 22.25),

    (iv) LOOK LEFT / RIGHT (paras 22.26 to 22.28),

    (v)   NO ENTRY and PLAY STREET (paras 22.29 to 22.33),

    (vi) police speed check (paras 22.34 to 22.38), and

    (vii) vehicle separation markings (paras 22.39 to 22.44).

Guidance on the formation of words, including the elongation of characters can be found in paras 22.45 to 22.50).

SLOW

22.2 The Regulations prescribe in diagram 1024 the word SLOW for use on the carriageway (see figure 22-1). It is prescribed in two sizes; 1600 mm intended for use where the speed limit is 40 mph or less, and 2800 mm where the speed limit is greater than 40 mph. Two smaller sizes are prescribed as diagram 1058.1 for use with cycle facilities (see paras 16.23 and 22.50).

22.3 Although the marking may be used alone, it is most effective when it complements a warning sign so that drivers are told why they need to slow down. The marking may be used with advance signs giving warning of STOP and GIVE WAY but not to supplement the GIVE WAY sign itself, for which the triangle marking to diagram 1023 is prescribed.

22.4 Discretion should be exercised in the use of the marking to ensure that its impact is not reduced

Diagram 1024

Figure 22-1

through proliferation. At particularly hazardous situations, e.g. on the approach to a bend at the end of a long straight section of high speed road, the marking may be repeated to give added emphasis.

HIGH VEHICLE MARKINGS AT ARCH BRIDGES

22.5 All bridges with a headroom of less than 16'-6" should be clearly signed. (Arch bridge signing is dealt with in Chapter 4, paras 7.16 to 7.19). Road markings, together with appropriate warning signs, can be used in the case of arch bridges to guide higher vehicles to the centre of the road, where the clearance may be greater than at the outside edges.

22.6 The HIGH VEHS marking (diagram 1024.1) is prescribed for use at arch bridges. High vehicles should be guided through the highest part of the arch using this marking and the arrow to diagram 1014, together with edge of carriageway markings to diagram 1010. These should be aligned with the chord marking on the bridge (diagram 532.2) which indicates the available headroom in the central part of the road. The lane or lanes passing under the bridge, together with edge lines, should be extended beyond the bridge for approximately 20 m to encourage long vehicles following the taper of the edge line to manoeuvre under the highest part of the structure and run straight until completely clear of it. In practice, site conditions may prevent the full lengths of markings being used but it should be the

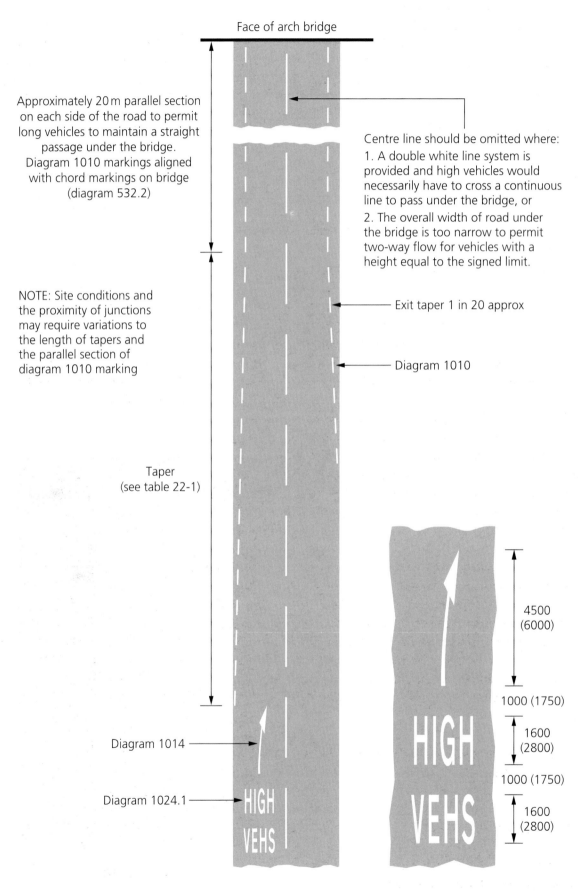

Face of arch bridge

Approximately 20 m parallel section on each side of the road to permit long vehicles to maintain a straight passage under the bridge. Diagram 1010 markings aligned with chord markings on bridge (diagram 532.2)

NOTE: Site conditions and the proximity of junctions may require variations to the length of tapers and the parallel section of diagram 1010 marking

Centre line should be omitted where:
1. A double white line system is provided and high vehicles would necessarily have to cross a continuous line to pass under the bridge, or
2. The overall width of road under the bridge is too narrow to permit two-way flow for vehicles with a height equal to the signed limit.

Exit taper 1 in 20 approx

Diagram 1010

Taper (see table 22-1)

Diagram 1014

Diagram 1024.1

HIGH VEHS

4500 (6000)

1000 (1750)

1600 (2800)

1000 (1750)

1600 (2800)

Figure 22-2

Table 22-1 Details of HIGH VEHS marking

Speed limit (mph)	Width of diagram 1010 marking	Taper of diagram 1010 marking	Length of arrow (mm)	Size of HIGH VEHS marking	Gap between legend/legend or legend/arrow
40 or less	100	1 in 40	4500	1600	1000
50 to 60	150	1 in 50	6000	2800	1750

aim to provide as nearly as possible the full length indicated in figure 22-2. Where the carriageway is sufficiently wide to permit two-way flow of low vehicles, the centre line should be continued through the bridge as a warning line; if there is insufficient width the line should be discontinued.

22.7 The area between the edge lines and the edge of carriageway must not be filled in with hatched lines. If all vehicles are required to adopt the centre path route, hatched markings to diagram 1040.4 should be used in place of diagram 1010.

22.8 If high vehicles are guided to the middle of a road on which a double white line system is in use, the double white lines must be discontinued under the bridge and replaced by a warning line, so that drivers of high vehicles do not commit an offence by crossing the marking to gain access to the highest part of the bridge.

22.9 A priority system using Give Way lines to diagram 1003 or shuttle working signals may be used, in which case the carriageway may be reduced to a single lane under the bridge. In addition to guiding high vehicles through the highest point of the arch and thereby reducing the risk of bridge strikes, this may also permit the provision of a new footway or the widening of an existing one under the bridge.

22.10 Details of the size and layout of the markings are shown in table 22-1.

KEEP CLEAR MARKINGS

22.11 Keep clear markings to indicate areas of the carriageway that should be kept clear of stationary vehicles are prescribed in three forms:

(i) diagram 1026, to allow the passage of vehicles into or out of a side road or access (see paras 22.12 to 22.14 and figure 22-3),

(ii) diagram 1026.1, to keep accesses and dropped kerbs clear (see paras 22.15 to 22.18 and figure 22-4), and

(iii) diagram 1027.1, to keep clear the access to a school, hospital or fire, police or ambulance station (see paras 22.19 to 22.25 and figure 22-5).

Diagram 1026

Figure 22-3

133

22.12 The advisory marking to diagram 1026 (see figure 22-3) is used mainly in urban areas where a queue of vehicles waiting at one junction blocks back across another, thereby obstructing the flow of cross traffic. It may also be used at a private entrance used by the general public, but only in places where it can genuinely be helpful in maintaining smooth traffic flow. It is not intended to keep areas of carriageway outside premises clear of parked vehicles.

22.13 The marking is prescribed in two sizes, the larger for use at particularly wide junctions or on multi-lane approaches. It is always coloured white.

22.14 The Regulations prescribe transverse lines to indicate the extent of the area to be kept clear of queuing vehicles where this is not obvious. They may be omitted if considered unnecessary, or if proximity to other markings or to traffic signals might cause confusion. Lines longer than prescribed must not be used; this can give the impression to side road traffic that vehicles on the main road are required to stop.

22.15 The marking to diagram 1026.1 (see figure 22-4) may be laid on part of the carriageway which should be kept clear of parked vehicles either outside an entrance to off-street premises, or where the kerb is dropped to provide a convenient crossing place for pedestrians.

22.16 It should normally be laid 75 mm wide for speed limits up to 40 mph and 100 mm when the limit is higher. The 50 mm size may be used in environmentally sensitive areas.

22.17 The marking is not legally enforceable. However, if used sparingly it may be helpful in discouraging inconsiderate parking, particularly where a problem is isolated and a traffic regulation order could not be justified or easily enforced. It may be used to mark the gaps across driveways between the ends of separate bays, except in controlled parking zones where every length of road outside the parking places must be marked with a yellow line (see para 20.29). This should reduce the risk of obstruction by non-residents, whilst avoiding the upright signs needed at each gap if a single yellow line were used instead (although signs would not be needed if double yellow lines were used). Yellow

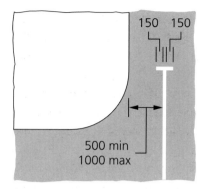

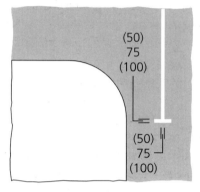

Diagram 1026.1

Figure 22-4

lines would however prevent residents from parking across their own driveways. The marking may also be used across a private entrance where there is a single yellow line, to keep the entrance clear at times when the restrictions are not in force; it should be laid on the carriageway side of the yellow line.

22.18 Where two or more closely spaced driveways are to be protected, it will be necessary to consider the distance between the markings to ensure it will accommodate at least one vehicle. An excessively long marking, or over-provision of markings will bring them into disrepute and compromise their effectiveness. The marking should not extend more than 1 m either side of the dropped kerb.

22.19 The KEEP CLEAR marking to diagram 1027.1 (see figure 22-5) is prescribed for use outside schools. This includes nurseries and playgroups, but where these occupy buildings other than schools, e.g. church or village halls, the word "SCHOOL" may be varied to "CHILDREN". "SCHOOL" must be omitted when the marking is used at fire, police or ambulance stations, or outside hospitals; these words must not however be used as part of the marking.

22.20 The overall length of the marking (using the word "SCHOOL") must not be less than 25.56 m nor more than 43.56 m. When the word "SCHOOL" is replaced by "CHILDREN", the maximum may be increased to 44.545 m. When the word "SCHOOL" and the short longitudinal line following it are omitted, two additional 3 m zig-zag modules are used symmetrically to give a minimum length of marking of 25.25 m. The overall length may be increased in increments of 6 m by the addition of a complete zig-zag module on each side up to the appropriate maximum. Further details may be found on the working drawing (see para 1.17).

22.21 The length of marking needs to be restricted to one which drivers will respect. Where an authority needs to mark a length greater than the maximum of 43.56 m, e.g. where the school is in a cul-de-sac or the marking is to extend across two entrances which are some distance apart, then two markings, varied in length if necessary (see para 22.20), may be used; they should be separated by a nominal gap of 100 mm. This will ensure that the legend is repeated at adequate intervals. When the marking is mandatory (see para 22.24) upright signs will be needed with each separate marking.

22.22 Where a larger gap would be safe, allowing at least 7 m between the two markings would provide a place for setting down children on their way to school. However, this might also encourage further vehicles to stop behind the first, and undermine compliance with the KEEP CLEAR marking.

22.23 The markings should not normally be placed on both sides of the road, but only on the side on which the entrance is situated. However, conditions may sometimes require otherwise, e.g. where there are school entrances on both sides of the road, or the road is so narrow that not to prevent parking on the opposite side to the school entrance is considered hazardous, or a patrol operates at that point.

22.24 The KEEP CLEAR marking is legally enforceable only when used in conjunction with an upright sign to diagram 642.2A and backed by a traffic regulation order. However, without regular enforcement action, the mandatory version is unlikely to be any better respected than the advisory marking.

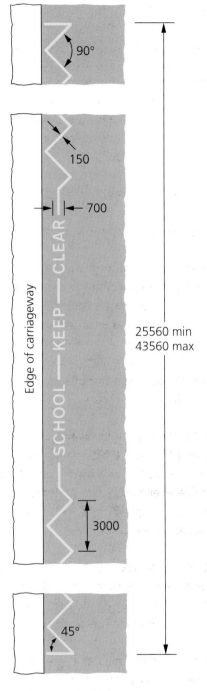

Diagram 1027.1

Figure 22-5

22.25 When the mandatory marking is used on a road where waiting restrictions apply, the yellow lines to diagram 1017 or 1018.1 are needed only if a restriction on the same length of road applies at times other than those covered by the stopping prohibition. If the KEEP CLEAR marking is advisory, yellow lines will always be needed if a waiting restriction is in force. The lines will be positioned between the KEEP CLEAR marking and the kerb. Similar rules apply to the use of "no loading" marks on the kerbs. In a controlled parking zone, yellow lines will always be required whether or not the KEEP CLEAR marking is mandatory.

LOOK LEFT / LOOK RIGHT

22.26 These markings are prescribed in diagram 1029 and illustrated in figure 22-6. They may be used at any point where pedestrians cross traffic approaching from an unexpected direction. This would include for example a pedestrian refuge in a one-way street, a channelising island where traffic in one direction passes on both sides, and places where pedestrians cross a contra-flow bus lane. They may also be used at Zebra, Pelican, Puffin or Toucan crossings and anywhere else it is considered that pedestrians need to be reminded of the direction of traffic flow.

22.27 The marking must never be used in a two-way street unless there is a central pedestrian refuge, or pedestrians will be misled into looking in the wrong direction once half way across.

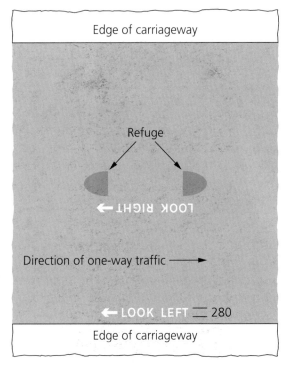

Diagram 1029

Figure 22-6

22.28 One size of marking is prescribed, being 280 mm in height using the non-elongated alphabet in Schedule 13 Part VI to the Regulations. It should be laid at a minimum distance of 150 mm from the edge of the carriageway. It should not replace or be superimposed upon a yellow line marking. The arrow is an integral part of the marking and must not be omitted.

NO ENTRY AND PLAY STREET

22.29 The NO ENTRY marking to diagram 1046 is generally used to supplement upright signs to diagram 616 (no entry for vehicular traffic). Except as specified in direction 7(3), these may be used only to indicate the effect of an Act, order, regulation, byelaw or notice. There are certain circumstances in which the marking may be used without upright signs, or without an order, but only at a site which has been approved in writing by the Secretary of State. Such approval will be given only where it is proposed to use the marking for safety reasons in circumstances where this would not prohibit an otherwise permitted movement. Further guidance can be found in para 22.32 and in Chapter 3.

22.30 Two patterns are prescribed in each of two sizes (see figure 22-7). The larger size (2800 mm) is for use at wide junctions. The marking may occupy one line or two, depending upon the space available.

22.31 Circumstances in which the marking might be helpful in supplementing upright No Entry signs which are supported by a traffic order include junctions where:

(i) the ahead movement is prohibited. The marking should be placed on the main carriageway side of the Give Way or Stop line opposite,

(ii) it may be difficult to see the upright signs, e.g. because of obscuration by stationary vehicles. The supplementary carriageway markings should help alert drivers before they become committed to the manoeuvre,

(iii) a single upright No Entry sign has been used, in accordance with direction 8, because the road is less than 5 m wide.

Marking NO ENTRY on the carriageway should help to reduce the risk of inadvertent non-compliance.

22.32 Purposes for which the marking might be used, either alone or to supplement No Entry signs, provided that the Secretary of State has given written approval to use the signs or markings in the absence of any statutory provision include:

(i) to prevent drivers taking the incorrect route past channelising traffic islands, e.g. when turning right at a side road junction. This procedure must not be used to prohibit completely the right turn at the junction. If this is necessary, a traffic regulation order must be made, and

(ii) to reduce the risk of traffic going the wrong way along a dual carriageway road or a slip road.

22.33 The marking may be varied to PLAY STREET and used with the upright signs to diagrams 617 and 618 at the start of a street where an appropriate traffic regulation order has been made.

POLICE SPEED CHECK MARKINGS

22.34 A standardised form of marking is prescribed as diagram 1063, in the shape of a square or circle (see figure 22-8). The square is preferred to the circle as it is less likely to be mistaken for a discarded hub cap etc. The maximum side length or diameter is prescribed as 600 mm.

22.35 The markings indicate the beginning and end of a measured distance over which the police can check vehicle speeds. The use of roadside features such as hazard markers or marks on safety barriers can lead to parallax problems. Markings on the carriageway can allow more accurate measurement, particularly from raised vantage points.

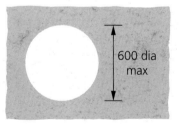

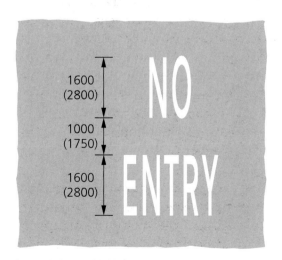

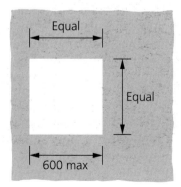

Diagram 1046

Figure 22-7

Diagram 1063

Figure 22-8

22.36 The marking may be placed on the carriageway only at the request of the police and may be used in as many lanes as required. In order to reduce maintenance costs it should be sited in the middle of the lane.

22.37 Other markings may be used in association with speed cameras, at the highway authority's discretion. They enable the distance a vehicle has moved in the time interval between two photographs to be measured and hence the speed calculated. Such markings are not considered to be traffic signs and are not prescribed in the Regulations.

22.38 The markings must not be laid in the controlled area of pedestrian crossings, or in positions that will interfere with other prescribed markings and cause possible confusion.

VEHICLE SEPARATION MARKINGS

22.39 The chevron markings to diagram 1064 (see figure 22-9) are prescribed for use on motorways only.

22.40 The marking is intended to remind drivers to keep a safe distance from the vehicle in front and has been shown to be beneficial in reducing accidents. Chevrons are placed at intervals of 40 metres, ensuring that a safe distance is kept between vehicles travelling at 70 mph as long as drivers keep a minimum of two chevrons apart.

22.41 The performance of chevrons at very high levels of traffic flow is not known. It is likely that most drivers will reduce their spacing (and ignore the chevrons) as flow levels increase. The average peak

hour flow encountered during trials was 4000 vehicles per hour. Caution should therefore be exercised when considering the use of chevrons at sites with higher flow levels.

22.42 The marking consists of a series of chevrons, marked in all lanes at the same 40 metre spacing, as indicated in figure 22-9. They should be laid over a distance of about 4 km, although this may be varied to between 3 km and 6 km.

22.43 The distance between successive series of chevrons should generally be between 40 km and 55 km. This need not be complied with rigidly, as specific site criteria are of greater importance. The start of a series of markings should be at least 1.6 km from the end of a previous entry slip road and should terminate at least 3.2 km before the next slip road. Significant gradients should be avoided. The Overseeing Department should be consulted if it is planned to use them on gradients steeper than 3%.

22.44 The Regulations require at least one sign to diagram 2933 "Keep apart 2 chevrons" to be used with the marking. However, a minimum of three such signs should normally be used, spaced at about

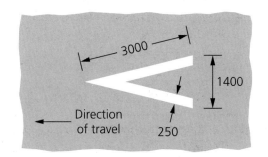

NOTE: Drainage gaps may be provided as appropriate

Diagram 1064

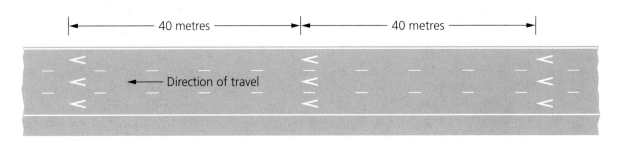

Figure 22-9

138

100 m, 1 km and 2 km after the start of the pattern. These distances may be regarded as approximate so that advantage may be taken of any existing safety fences. A sign to diagram 2934 "Check your distance" must be provided, and placed about 300 m before the commencement of the markings, with the variant "Keep your distance" about 300 m after they terminate. These should normally have an x-height of 250 mm on dual two-lane motorways and 300 mm on dual three or four-lane motorways.

FORMATION OF WORDS

22.45 The basic characters for worded road markings are the capital letters, numerals, apostrophe and the ampersand from the Transport Medium alphabet, enlarged and where appropriate elongated to two standard sizes. The alphabets are shown in Part VI of Schedule 13 to the Regulations.

22.46 To ensure correct letter spacing when forming a word, the characters are placed on imaginary tiles which vary in width according to the size of the character and the tiles butted up to each other to make the legend. The tile width for each letter is shown in table 22-2. The distance between the tiles of separate words (e.g. NO ENTRY when marked on a single line) is 400 mm, measured to the edge of the tiles and not to the actual characters.

Table 22-3 Elongated legends

Diagram Number	Legend
1022	STOP
1024	SLOW
1024.1	HIGH VEHS
1025.1	BUS STOP, BUS STAND
1025.3	BUS STOP, BUS STAND
1025.4	BUS STOP, BUS STAND
1026	KEEP CLEAR
1035	Lane destinations
1036.1	TURN LEFT
1036.2	AHEAD ONLY
1037.1	TURN RIGHT
1046	NO ENTRY
1048	BUS LANE
1048.1	BUS AND (cycle symbol) LANE
1048.2	TRAM & BUS ONLY
1048.3	BUS ONLY
1048.4	BUS AND (cycle symbol) ONLY
1058	END
1058.1	SLOW
1065	Speed limit

NOTE: Diagrams 1058 and 1058.1 are prescribed in special sizes and may be used only for cycle facilities.

Table 22-2 Tile widths

Letter	Width (mm)	Letter	Width (mm)	Letter	Width (mm)
A	544	N	672	1	316
B	588	O	624	2	480
C	592	P	520	3	508
D	616	Q	632	4	528
E	528	R	564	5	488
F	476	S	548	6	504
G	620	T	436	7	416
H	640	U	616	8	520
I	292	V	520	9	512
J	372	W	732	0	532
K	552	X	512	'	156
L	428	Y	492	&	504
M	736	Z	476	/	312

Table 22-4 Non-elongated legends

Diagram Number	Legend
1027.1	SCHOOL / CHILDREN KEEP CLEAR
	KEEP CLEAR
1028.2	TAXIS, POLICE, AMBULANCES
1028.3	BUSES, DISABLED
	LARGE OR SLOW VEHICLES ONLY
	LOADING ONLY
1028.4	DOCTOR
	SOLO MOTORCYCLES ONLY
	SOLO M/CYCLES ONLY
	SOLO M/CS ONLY
	PERMIT HOLDERS ONLY
1029	LOOK LEFT, LOOK RIGHT
1033	DISABLED

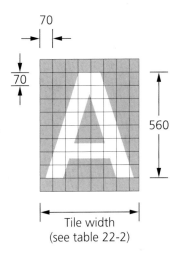

70

70

560

Tile width
(see table 22-2)

Base character from the Transport Medium
alphabet. Capital letter height is 560 mm
(equivalent x-height of 400 mm). Tile width
is the same as that used on vertical signs.

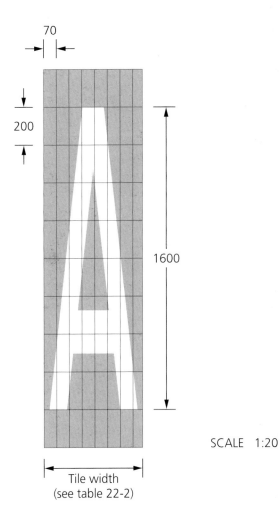

70

200

1600

Tile width
(see table 22-2)

Road markings to Schedule 13 Part IV (a)
of the Regulations (base character elongated
vertically by a factor of 200/70)

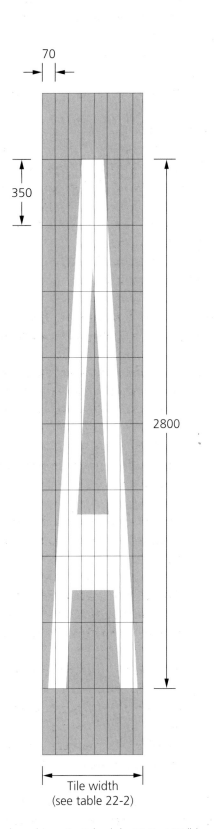

70

350

2800

Tile width
(see table 22-2)

Road markings to Schedule 13 Part IV (b)
of the Regulations (base character elongated
vertically by a factor of 350/70)

SCALE   1:20

Figure 22-10

22.47 Worded road markings placed transversely across the carriageway (see table 22-3) are elongated in the longitudinal direction, keeping the transverse dimension unchanged. This makes it easier for a driver to read the legend. Those not so placed are listed in table 22-4; these are not elongated.

22.48 Figure 22-10 shows how elongation is achieved, using the letter "A" as an example. The base character is taken from the Transport Medium alphabet at an x-height of 400 mm and therefore a capital letter height of 560 mm (see Chapter 7, para 2.8). The letter is drawn on a grid measuring 70 x 70 mm (i.e. 560/8). The 1600 mm size character is elongated in the ratio of 200/70 and the 2800 mm size in the ratio of 350/70.

22.49 To set out an elongated worded marking on the carriageway, the following method is suggested:

(i) determine how much of the carriageway width is available for the word, allowing a minimum of 300 mm clear at either side,

(ii) decide on the size of the alphabet required from the appropriate section of this chapter,

(iii) add up the tile widths from table 22-2 to determine the overall width of the marking,

(iv) if this width is less than that calculated at (i) above, then the word may be positioned centrally within the width available,

(v) if the width is more than that calculated at (i) above, then a suitable abbreviation will need to be considered where permitted, e.g. for lane destinations. Prescribed markings such as SLOW must not be abbreviated.

22.50 Diagrams 1058 (END) and 1058.1 (SLOW) are for use on cycle facilities and are therefore reduced in size. The width of the marking (excluding the outside edge of the first and last tiles) is prescribed in the Regulations. These markings do not follow the standard rules for elongation outlined above.

23 MATERIALS AND MAINTENANCE

GENERAL

23.1 Road marking materials and road studs are specified in the appropriate British Standards. These are generally the English language versions of standards published by the European Committee for Standardisation (CEN).

ROAD MARKING MATERIALS

23.2 Road markings are applied using thermoplastic, cold plastic, preformed material or paint. They may be laid as permanent markings or as temporary markings at road works.

23.3 Thermoplastic material is applied hot and sets on laying. It may be applied by a hand or mechanical applicator. It has good durability and is suitable for use on all roads. Mechanical application is most suitable for use on motorways and other high standard roads where it can be laid in long runs using motorised equipment with minimum disruption to traffic.

23.4 Cold plastics are supplied in single or multi-component forms. The product is laid on the carriageway and a cohesive film is formed by chemical action.

23.5 Preformed thermoplastic road markings are applied by heating the material until it bonds to the road surface by melting or fusion. They provide a simple way to apply arrows, lettering etc. and to reinstate short lengths of line without the need for substantial application and support equipment.

23.6 Preformed cold plastic material is applied to the road surface using an adhesive.

23.7 Preformed tape is produced in sheet or roll form and is either bonded to the road surface or inlaid. Pressure is applied, but not heat. Preformed markings have good durability, are of uniform thickness and do not spread in hot weather or under the weight of heavy traffic. They can be difficult to apply to some surface dressings and block paviors. They are also manufactured in an easily removable form for use at road works.

23.8 Paint is best restricted to roads where the markings are not subject to heavy traffic wear. It is particularly suitable for edge lining, for yellow waiting restriction lines and for parking bays as, being thinner than thermoplastic material, it will not interfere with drainage. The ease and safety in handling paint compared to thermoplastic material, its suitability for laying with motorised equipment and the material's low initial cost, makes paint an attractive economic proposition for such applications.

EUROPEAN AND BRITISH STANDARDS

23.9 Initial laboratory requirements for materials are described in BS EN 1790 for preformed markings and BS EN 1871 for directly laid materials. Requirements for drop-on materials (glass beads and anti-skid aggregates) and premix glass beads are dealt with in BS EN 1423 and 1424 respectively. BS EN 1436 specifies several performance levels for properties such as retroreflectivity, skid resistance and durability. Materials will be classified in accordance with the relevant standard following performance testing. In the UK, this will normally be on the basis of laboratory tests to BS EN 1790 or BS EN 1871 as appropriate, and road trials to BS EN 1824.

23.10 The Specification for Highway Works published by the Stationery Office specifies which performance classes in BS EN 1436 for luminance factor, skid resistance and retroreflectivity are to be used on trunk roads and motorways. As higher retroreflective performance requires additional glass beads, which will reduce the skid resistance, it is not practicable to specify the highest performance class for both. A judgement will need to be made as to which property is more important at any particular location.

23.11 Initial performance requirements for road studs are described in BS EN 1463-1 and the specification for road trials in BS EN 1463-2. The performance levels and classes are listed in BS EN 1463-1. Minimum performance levels to be achieved for use on UK roads are prescribed in the Traffic Signs Regulations and General Directions 2002 (direction 57). Guidance on the correct use of road studs will be found in section 6.

23.12 The following British Standards have been withdrawn as a result of the introduction of European standards:

BS 3262: Parts 1, 2 and 3: 1989 Hot applied thermoplastic road marking materials,

BS 6044: 1987 Pavement marking paints,

BS 6088: 1981 Solid glass beads for use with road marking compounds and for other industrial uses (those sections relating to glass beads for road marking materials),

PD 6518: 1987 Prefabricated temporary road marking materials for use at road works,

BS 7396: 1991 Permanent preformed road markings.

23.13 British Standard BS 7962: 2000 sets out performance requirements for black masking materials. It is not planned to replace this with a European standard.

REFLECTORISATION

23.14 Road markings fall into two categories, those which must be illuminated with retroreflecting material, and those which may be so illuminated (regulation 31). Table 23-1 lists the diagram numbers of markings which must be reflectorised.

23.15 It is not usually necessary to reflectorise waiting restriction lines as they do not normally have a guidance function. However, reflectorisation may be advantageous where such lines are used on the rural outskirts of a town and the road edge is unkerbed, or where a reflectorised edge of carriageway marking immediately precedes such markings. If the yellow lines are reflectorised, any associated parking bays should be also.

23.16 Reflectorisation is achieved by adding glass beads to the markings. These reflect light from vehicle headlamps back towards the driver, making the markings much brighter than they would otherwise be. Beads are normally premixed into the material. It is only when some of the material has worn away to expose the beads that they become fully effective; to overcome this, glass beads are also applied to the surface as "drop-on material" as the marking is laid. The retroreflection of a marking in wet conditions can be enhanced by providing a prominent surface texture. These profiled markings incorporate a series of near-vertical edges which keep the glass beads clear of the water film which would otherwise largely negate the retroreflective property. BS EN 1436 provides specifiers with several classes of wet performance. Profiled markings may be either of the raised rib type prescribed as diagrams 1012.2 and 1012.3, or may consist of an embossed pattern in the material. Provided this latter type is no thicker than 6 mm overall, it may be applied to any marking. In the case of raised rib markings, the passage of wheels also generally produces an acoustic or vibratory effect (see paras 4.39 to 4.48). Improved visibility in all weather conditions may also be achieved by using a wider line where alternatives are prescribed (see paras 1.13 and 1.14).

Table 23-1 Markings required to be reflectorised

1001[1]	1008	1023 [2]	1041
1001.1	1008.1	1024	1041.1
1001.2	1009	1024.1	1042
1002.1	1010	1036.1	1042.1
1003 [2]	1012.1	1036.2	1046
1003.1	1012.2	1037.1	1049 [2]
1003.3	1012.3	1039	1062
1003.4	1013.1	1040	1064
1004	1013.3	1040.2	1065
1004.1	1013.4	1040.3	
1005	1014	1040.4	
1005.1	1022	1040.5	

NOTES
1. Except when used in conjunction with diagram 1001.3.
2. Except when varied to smallest size for use on a cycle track.

STATUTORY COLOURS

23.17 The colours white and yellow are prescribed for road marking materials. Black material may also be used to mask existing markings, where these need to be temporarily obscured during road works (see para 23.13).

23.18 The standard colour for yellow markings is BS 381C No.355 (lemon); No.309 (canary) is also acceptable. In environmentally sensitive areas, yellow markings to No.310 (primrose) or No.353 (deep cream) may be preferred. Special authorisation is not necessary for any of these shades. Different shades should not be used on adjacent lines, as in certain conditions the lighter colour may appear white when seen in direct comparison with the standard yellow.

APPLICATION OF MARKINGS

23.19 As it is not possible to lay road markings to precise dimensions, and to allow for markings "spreading" in service, some tolerance in the prescribed dimensions is permitted by regulation 12. Specified values may vary by up to 5° for angular measurements and by the tolerances quoted in table 23-2 for linear dimensions. No tolerance is permitted for those angular or linear dimensions which are expressed as a maximum or minimum value. A tolerance of plus or minus 25 mm is normally allowed in the lateral positioning of lane lines.

23.20 It is essential that all types of marking should be skid resistant in wet conditions. This is particularly important where the camber or cross fall is steep, and at junctions. The Specification for Highway Works requires a skid resistance value of not less than 45 (sub-clause 1212.3), except in certain locations where the designer may select a value of not less than 55

(sub-clause 1212.6). This higher value should be used for yellow bar markings (see para 11.7) and it would also be appropriate to use it for other markings which might pose a hazard to a braking vehicle.

MAINTENANCE

23.21 Road markings, including reflecting road studs, must be well maintained if they are to fulfil their purpose. Regulatory markings must be maintained properly if they are to be enforced effectively. Guidance can be found in TD 26 in Volume 8 of the Design Manual for Roads and Bridges (see para 1.4).

23.22 All markings, including reflecting road studs, should be inspected at regular intervals both by day and, where appropriate, for reflectance by night. Retroreflectivity of road markings can be measured by static equipment or by dynamic equipment mounted on a vehicle travelling at normal traffic speeds.

23.23 It is not possible to recommend specific renewal intervals for markings as these will depend upon the type of line, the material comprising the marking and traffic flow. Traffic authorities should keep their carriageway markings under review (particularly on heavily-trafficked roads) to ensure that their effectiveness is maintained at all times.

23.24 Markings should be renewed as soon as possible after resurfacing or on the completion of road works which may have damaged them. Where it is not practicable to restore them immediately using permanent materials, a temporary marking should be used, particularly at sites such as road junctions, if the absence of a marking might give rise to dangerous conditions. Arrangements should be made to protect road studs during surface dressing operations.

Table 23-2 Road marking tolerances

Dimension shown in the diagrams	Allowable tolerance
3 m or more	Up to 15% greater than or 10% less than the specified dimension
300 mm or more, but less than 3 m	Up to 20% greater than or 10% less than the specified dimension
50 mm or more, but less than 300 mm	Up to 30% greater than or 10% less than the specified dimension

23.25 Where it is not possible to provide temporary road markings, drivers should be warned of their absence by means of advance warning signs. At junctions where all, or any part, of the STOP or Give Way marking has been removed and temporary markings cannot be provided, a prescribed variant of diagram 7012 "NO STOP MARKINGS" or "NO GIVE WAY MARKINGS" should be placed on the minor road near the junction, preferably about 5-10 m from the edge of the main carriageway. Where road markings associated with a level crossing are absent, the variant "NO ROAD MARKINGS AT LEVEL CROSSING" should be used. The alternative legends "NO ROAD MARKINGS" and "NO ROAD MARKINGS AT JUNCTION" should be used where appropriate. Where lane lines or centre of carriageway lines on inter-urban roads have been removed (especially where there is no street lighting), a sign bearing the legend "NO ROAD MARKINGS FOR X MILES" or "X YARDS" or, if appropriate, "NO ROAD STUDS FOR X MILES" or "X YARDS" (diagram 7012) should be used with the appropriate distance inserted.

23.26 All obsolete markings and road stud housings, particularly those which may give a misleading indication, should be removed as soon as possible. This is particularly important where new central refuges are installed; the old centre line and any road studs should *always* be realigned (see table 14-1 for recommended tapers) before the road works signing and guarding is removed.

DRAINAGE

23.27 It is essential that road markings should not prevent a carriageway from draining properly. Even a thin film of standing water can be dangerous in the winter, when it may freeze. Markings may project up to 6 mm above the adjacent road surface (regulation 32), although the ribs of raised rib markings and the centre portion of diagrams 1003.4 and 1049.1 may be higher. In difficult areas, where for instance the cross fall is nearly level, or the road is at the lowest point of a sag curve, it may be preferable to use paint in place of thermoplastic for continuous edge lines, as its negligible thickness will

not obstruct the flow of surface water. However, this may not be practicable if the markings will be heavily trafficked, as paint is not very durable, and it might be preferable to leave short gaps in the marking to aid drainage.

23.28 Generally a drainage channel of 225 mm should be maintained between markings and the kerbed edge of a road. This will allow water to flow freely and help to ensure that the markings do not become unnecessarily dirty.

APPENDIX A: Northern Ireland variations

The Traffic Signs Regulations and General Directions 2002 apply to England, Wales and Scotland, but in Northern Ireland the equivalent legislation is the Traffic Signs Regulations (Northern Ireland) 1997. In Northern Ireland, references to "Directions" are not applicable; where these are referred to, advice should be sought from the Roads Service Transportation Unit, Department for Regional Development in Belfast.

The following table indicates differences in regulation numbers between the two sets of Regulations where these are relevant to this chapter of the Traffic Signs Manual. The notes below indicate other differences of legislation or practice between Northern Ireland and the rest of the UK.

Paragraph number in Chapter 5	Meaning	Regulation in the Traffic Signs Regulations and General Directions 2002	Regulation in the Traffic Signs Regulations (Northern Ireland) 1997
3.1	Legal meaning of the STOP sign	16	14
3.1	Legal meaning of the Give Way marking	25(2)	24(2)
4.49	Proportional dimensions of hatched markings	12(4)	10(4)
5.1	Double white lines; legal requirements and exemptions	26	25
6.15	Colour of non-reflective road studs	11(4)	9(4)
12.1	Legal meaning of yellow box	29(2)	26
23.19	Road marking tolerances	12	10

In the following notes, paragraph numbers refer to this edition of Chapter 5 of the Traffic Signs Manual.

Paragraphs 2.4, 5.7 and 12.4 In Northern Ireland, "Section 36 of the Road Traffic Act 1988" should be replaced with "Article 50 of the Road Traffic (Northern Ireland) Order 1995, as amended by Article 75(1) and item 19 of Schedule 8 to the Road Traffic Regulation (Northern Ireland) Order 1997".

Paragraph 4.27 In Northern Ireland, policy on the use of edge of carriageway markings and associated road studs is currently being developed. Advice should therefore be sought from the Roads Service Transportation Unit, Department for Regional Development, Belfast.

Paragraph 11.3 In Northern Ireland, yellow bar markings are prescribed as diagram 1003.6, but only for use at roundabouts on dual carriageway roads. The dimension from the Give Way line to the first bar is prescribed as either 35 m or 50 m.

Paragraph 15.1 In Northern Ireland, the relevant Regulations are the Zebra Pedestrian Crossings Regulations (Northern Ireland) 1974 and the Pelican Pedestrian Crossings Regulations (Northern Ireland) 1989. Puffin and Toucan crossings in Northern Ireland are authorised on a site by site basis.

Paragraph 16.20 In the Northern Ireland Regulations, the cycle reservoir is numbered 1001.1.

Paragraph 18.12 In the Northern Ireland Regulations, the tram stop line is numbered 1001.2.

Paragraph 21.7 In the Northern Ireland Regulations, markings on humps and cushions are prescribed as composite layouts in diagrams 1060, 1060.1, 1061, 1061.1 and 1062. Elsewhere in the UK, the triangular hump marking is prescribed separately as diagram 1062; it may be used in conjunction with other prescribed markings as appropriate.

APPENDIX B: Index of diagrams

INDEX

Printed in the United Kingdom for TSO N167610 C12 04/4 957445